书虫·牛津英汉对照读物

曾达的囚徒
The Prisoner of Zenda

Anthony Hope

Diane Mowat 改写

黄宏 译

外语教学与研究出版社
牛津大学出版社

（京）新登字 155 号

京权图字 01－97－0346

图书在版编目（CIP）数据

曾达的囚徒/(英)霍普(Hope, A.)著；黄宏译. －北京：外语教学
与研究出版社，1997.10
（书虫·牛津英汉对照读物）
ISBN 7－5600－1295－7

Ⅰ.曾…　Ⅱ.①霍…②黄…　Ⅲ.小说－对照读物－英、汉
Ⅳ.H319.4：Ⅰ

中国版本图书馆 CIP 数据核字(97)第 17697 号

曾达的囚徒
著 Anthony Hope
译 黄宏
＊　　＊　　＊
外语教学与研究出版社出版发行
（北京西三环北路 19 号　100089）
http://www.fltrp.com.cn
北京博诚印刷厂印刷
开本 850×1092　1/32　3.25 印张
1998 年 1 月第 1 版　2002 年 8 月第 6 次印刷
印数：186001—236000 册
＊　　＊　　＊
ISBN 7－5600－1295－7/H·733
定价：3.90 元

简 介

　　鲁道夫·拉森狄尔年轻富有,出生于一个历史悠久的英国家庭,可他却长着卢里塔尼亚王室所特有的深红色头发和长而笔挺的鼻子。这是多年前一个小小的家庭"意外"造成的结果。

　　鲁道夫决定去参加卢里塔尼亚新国王的加冕典礼。他到了曾达城,并在森林里漫步。第二天上午他却发现自己身陷意想不到的奇遇之中。他与新朋友萨普特上尉和弗里茨一起制定了营救曾达城堡中的囚徒的计划。很快他就与国王的死对头黑迈克和鲁帕特交上了手,而且爱上了国王的表妹,美丽的弗蕾维亚公主。

　　然后国王……然而,谁才是真正的卢里塔尼亚的国王呢?

　　安东尼·霍普 1863 年生于伦敦,1933 年去世。他的真名是安东尼·霍普·霍金斯爵士。他成为专职作家之前是一位律师。他最著名的作品有《曾达的囚徒》和《鲁帕特》。

1

1

The Rassendylls – and the Elphbergs

'I wonder when you're going to do something useful, Rudolf,' my brother's wife said. She looked at me crossly over the breakfast table.

'But why should I do anything, Rose?' I answered, calmly eating my egg. 'I've got nearly enough money for the things I want, and my brother, Robert, is a lord – Lord Burlesdon. I'm very happy.'

'You're twenty-nine, and you've done nothing except...'

'Play about? It's true. We Rassendylls are a rich and famous family, and we don't need to do anything.'

This made Rose angry. 'Rich and famous families usually behave worse than less important families,' she said.

When I heard this, I touched my dark red hair. I knew what she meant.

'I'm so pleased that Robert's hair is black!' she cried.

Just then my brother, Robert, came in. When he looked at Rose, he could see that there was something wrong.

'What's the matter, my dear?' he said.

'Oh, she's angry because I never do anything useful, and because I've got red hair,' I said.

'Well, I know he can't do much about his hair, or his nose...' Rose began.

'No, the nose and the hair are in the family,' my brother a-

2

1 拉森狄尔家族与艾尔弗伯格家族

"我在想你究竟什么时候才会做一些有用的事儿，鲁道夫。"我的嫂嫂说。她在餐桌的那头生气地望着我。

"但我干嘛要做事呢，罗丝?"我一边回答她，一边从容地吃着鸡蛋。"我的钱够多的，差不多想要什么就能买什么，再说我哥哥罗伯特又是一位贵族——伯利斯顿勋爵，我挺幸福。"

"可你都29岁了，你还什么都没干，除了……"

"除了胡闹? 你说对了，我们拉森狄尔家的人又有钱又有名，而且我们什么也不用做。"

我这么说让罗丝生气了。"又有钱又有名的人家通常比那些普通人家更不规矩!"

听了她的话，我用手摸摸我的深红色头发。我懂她的意思。

"我真高兴罗伯特的头发是黑色的!"她说道。

正在此时，我哥哥罗伯特走了进来，他一看罗丝，就看出有些不对头。

"怎么了，亲爱的?"他问道。

"她生气了，因为我从没做过什么有用的事儿，而且我还长着红头发。"我说。

"当然，我知道他对他的头发和鼻子无能为力……"罗丝说。

"是的，这样的鼻子和这样的头发是祖

the Rassendylls, the Rassendyll family: 姓拉森狄尔的，拉森狄尔家族。
crossly *adv. angrily.* 生气，发怒。**lord** *n. a nobleman of high rank. (less important than a duke)* 勋爵，地位次于公爵。*Lord Burlesdon*，伯利斯顿勋爵。**play about:** *to spend time having fun.* 胡闹，鬼混。**in the family:** *(a quality) shared by several members of a family, or passed from parents to children.* 指某种性格特征等为某些家族成员所共有的或祖辈相传的。

greed. 'And Rudolf has both of them. '

In the room there were many family pictures, and one of them was of a very beautiful woman, Lady Amelia, who lived a hundred and fifty years ago. I stood up and turned to look at it.

'If you took that picture away, Robert, ' Rose cried, 'we could forget all about it. '

'Oh, but I don't want to forget about it, ' I replied. 'I like being an Elphberg. '

But perhaps I should stop for a moment and explain why Rose was angry about my nose and my hair — and why I, a Rassendyll, said I was an Elphberg. After all, the Elphbergs are the royal family of Ruritania, and have been for hundreds of years.

The story is told in a book about the Rassendyll family history.

In the year 1733 Prince Rudolf of Ruritania came to England on a visit and he stayed for several months. Like many of the Elphberg royal family, he had blue eyes, an unusually long straight nose and a lot of dark red hair. He was also tall and very good-looking.

During his stay here, he became friendly with Lady Amelia, the beautiful wife of Lord Burlesdon. They became very good friends indeed, which, naturally, did not please Lord Burlesdon. So, one cold wet morning, the two men fought. The Prince was hurt in the fight, but got better and was hurried back to

4

传的,"我哥哥同意她的话,"而且鲁道夫两样都占了。"

房间里有很多家族成员的画像,其中一幅画着一位非常美丽的女人,阿米莉亚夫人,她生活在 150 年以前。我站了起来,转身去看她。

"如果你把那画像拿走,罗伯特,"罗丝说,"我们就可以把这件事忘掉。"

"哦,可是我并不想忘掉它。"我回答。"我喜欢做艾尔弗伯格家族的一员。"

也许我应该停下来一会儿,解释一下为什么罗丝对我的鼻子和头发那么生气,究竟又为什么,我,一个姓拉森狄尔的,会说我自己是艾尔弗伯格家族的一员。毕竟艾尔弗伯格家族是卢里塔尼亚的王族,而且,几百年来一直如此。

这个故事在一本关于拉森狄尔家族史的书里是这么描述的:

1733 年卢里塔尼亚王子鲁道夫前来英国访问,他逗留了几个月。像艾尔弗伯格王室的许多人一样,他长着蓝色的眼睛,一只不寻常的又长又挺的鼻子和很多深红色的头发。他个子很高,相貌英俊。

他在此地停留期间,与伯利斯顿勋爵美丽的妻子阿米莉亚夫人结识,事实上,他俩成了十分亲密的好友,这当然不会让伯利斯顿勋爵愉快。因此,在一个寒冷潮湿的早晨,两位男士决斗了。王子负了伤,但很快

royal *adj . for, belong to, or connected with a king or queen .* 皇族的,王室的。

5

Ruritania. There he married and became King Rudolf the Third. But Lord Burlesdon fell ill, and six months later he died. Two months after that, Lady Amelia had a baby son, who became the next Lord Burlesdon and the head of the Rassendyll family. The boy grew into a man with blue eyes, a long straight nose, and dark red hair.

These things can happen in the best of families, and among the many pictures of the Rassendylls at home, you can see that five or six of them have the same blue eyes, the same nose, and the same red hair.

So, because my hair was red and I had the Elphberg nose, Rose worried about me. In the end, to please her, I promised to get a job in six months' time. This gave me six free months to enjoy myself first.

And an idea came to me – I would visit Ruritania. None of my family had ever been there. They preferred to forget all about the Lady Amelia. But I saw in the newspaper that, in three weeks, the new young King, Rudolf the Fifth, would have his coronation. It would be an interesting time to visit the country.

I knew my family would not like my going, so I told them I was going walking in Austria.

好转并且匆匆返回卢里塔尼亚。在那里他
结了婚,成了国王鲁道夫三世。但是伯利斯
顿勋爵病了,六个月以后去世。他辞世之后
两个月,阿米莉亚夫人生了一个儿子,这个
男孩即成为新的伯利斯顿勋爵以及拉森狄
尔家族的首领。他成人以后有着蓝色的眼
睛,长而挺直的鼻子和深红色的头发。

这一类的事情可能在最上流的家庭发
生。在拉森狄尔府上的许多画像中,你能看
见五六个人长着同样的蓝眼睛,同样的鼻
子,同样的红头发。

因此,由于我的头发是红的,而且我长
着艾尔弗伯格家的鼻子,罗丝为我发愁。结
果,为了让她高兴,我保证六个月以内找到
一份工作。这样起码我能在六个月的时间
里过得快快乐乐的。

我有了一个主意——我要去卢里塔尼
亚。我的家族从来没有一个人去过那里。
他们更愿意忘记跟阿米莉亚夫人有关的事
情。可是我看到报纸上说,在三周之内,卢
里塔尼亚的年轻的新国王,鲁道夫五世,将
会举行加冕典礼。这时候去这个国家看看
一定很有意思。

我知道家里的人一定不喜欢让我去,所
以我告诉他们我要去奥地利走走。

to please sb.: *to make sb. happy.* 使……感到快乐。
to enjoy oneself: *to be happy.* 感到快乐。**coronation** *n. the ceremony at which a king, queen, ruling prince, etc., is crowned.* 国王、女王、王子等的加冕典礼。

2
The colour of men's hair

On the way to Ruritania I decided to spend a night in Paris with a friend. The next morning he came with me to the station, and as we waited for the train, we watched the crowds. We noticed a tall, dark, very fashionable lady, and my friend told me who she was.

'That's Madame Antoinette de Mauban. She's travelling on the same train as you, but don't fall in love with her.'

'Why not?' I asked, amused.

'Ah,' said my friend, 'all Paris knows that she's in love with Duke Michael of Strelsau. And he, as you know, is the half-brother of the new King of Ruritania. Although he's only the second son and will never be king himself, he's still an important man and very popular, I hear, with many Ruritanians. The lovely Madame Antoinette won't look twice at you, Rudolf.'

I laughed, but he had woken my interest in the lady. I did not speak to her during the journey, and when we arrived in Ruritania, I left the train at Zenda, a small town outside the capital. But I noticed that Madame de Mauban went on to Strelsau, the capital.

I was welcomed very kindly at my hotel. It belonged to a fat old lady and her pretty daughter. From them I learned that the coronation was to be on the day after next, and not in three

8

2 头发的颜色

去卢里塔尼亚的途中我决定在巴黎的一个朋友处过一夜。第二天早晨他跟我一起来到火车站，等车时我们看着站台上的人群，我们看到一位个子高、肤色棕黑、非常时髦的女士。我的朋友告诉我她的身份。

"那位是安东纳特·德·莫班女士，她和你坐同一列火车，但是你可别爱上她。"

"为什么不行?"我觉得很有意思。

"哎呀，"我的朋友说，"全巴黎都知道她爱着斯特莱索的迈克尔公爵，他是卢里塔尼亚新国王同父异母的兄弟。虽然他只不过是次子，他也决不能当国王，他仍然是个重要人物，而且我听说他也受到许多人的爱戴。鲁道夫，那位可爱的安冬纳特女士不会朝你看第二眼的。"

我笑了，但他的话引起了我对那位女士的兴趣。旅途中我没跟她说话。我们到达卢里塔尼亚以后，我在靠近首都的小城曾达下了车，但我注意到莫班女士去了首都斯特莱索。

在旅店我受到了很热情的接待。这家旅店是一位胖老太太和她可爱的女儿开的。从她们那儿我听说加冕典礼是后天而不是三星期后举行。

fashionable adj. (made, dressed, etc.) according to the latest fashion. (打扮、服装等)流行的，时髦的。**to fall in love** (with): become filled with love. 爱上某人。**amuse** v. make (sb) laugh or smile. (使人)感到好笑，有趣。**duke** n. nobleman of high rank (next below a prince). 公爵，地位仅次于王子。**half brother**: brother by one parent only. 同父异母(或同母异父)的兄弟。**popular** adj. well liked. 受欢迎的，受爱戴的。**pretty** adj. pleasing and charming without being beautiful or grand. 可爱的，悦目的(并非华丽堂皇)。

9

weeks.

The old lady was more interested in Duke Michael of Strelsau than in the new King. The Castle of Zenda and all the land around it belonged to the Duke, but the old lady said, 'It's not enough. Duke Michael should be king. He spends all his time with us. Every Ruritanian knows him, but we never see the new King.'

But the daughter cried, 'Oh no, I hate Black Michael. I want a red Elphberg – and the King, our friend Johann says, is very red. Johann works for the Duke and he's seen the King. In fact, the King's staying just outside Zenda now,' she added. 'He's resting at the Duke's house in the forest before going on to Strelsau on Wednesday for his coronation. The Duke's already in Strelsau, getting everything ready.'

'They're friends?' I asked.

'Friends who want the same place and the same wife,' the pretty girl replied. 'The Duke wants to marry his cousin, Princess Flavia, but people say she's going to be King Rudolf's wife and the Queen.'

Just then their friend, Johann, entered the room.

'We have a visitor, Johann,' the girl's mother said, and Johann turned towards me. But when he saw me, he stepped back, with a look of wonder on his face.

'What's the matter, Johann?' the daughter asked.

'Good evening, sir,' Johann said, still staring at me. He did not seem to like what he saw.

10

老太太对迈克尔公爵比对新国王更感兴趣。虽然曾达城堡和附近所有的土地都属于这位公爵，老太太却说，"这些还不够，迈克尔公爵应该当国王。他总是和我们在一起，每个卢里塔尼亚人都认识他，而新国王我们却从来没见过。"

她女儿却说，"哦，不，我讨厌黑迈克尔！我希望一个红头发的艾尔弗伯格当国王。听我们的朋友约翰说，新国王的头发非常红。他见过国王。事实上，国王现在就在曾达。"她又说，"他星期五去斯特莱索加冕。在此之前，他呆在公爵的林中住地休养。公爵已经去了斯特莱索，为国王准备好一切。"

"他们是朋友吗？"

"朋友，只不过两人想得到同样的地方和同一个女人。"漂亮姑娘回答，"公爵想和他的表妹弗蕾维亚公主结婚，可是据说弗蕾维亚会成为国王鲁道夫的妻子和王后。"

就在这时，她们的朋友约翰走进了房间。

"我们来了个客人，约翰。"姑娘的母亲说。约翰就转向我。当他看见我后，他后退了一步，脸上露出惊奇的表情。

"怎么啦？"姑娘问。

"晚上好，先生。"约翰说，仍然紧盯着我。他看上去不喜欢他所看见的东西。

cousin *n.* *the child of one's uncle or aunt.* 表兄弟或表姐妹，堂兄弟或堂姐妹。**look** *n.* *facial expression.* 表情。**stare** (**at**) *v.* *to look fixedly with wide-opened eyes.* 紧紧盯着。

The girl began to laugh. 'It's the colour of your hair, sir,' she explained. 'We don't often see that colour here. It's the Elphberg red — not Johann's favourite colour.'

*　　　*　　　*

The next day I decided to walk through the forest for a few miles and take the train to Strelsau from a little station along the road. I sent my luggage on by train and after lunch, I started out on foot. First, I wanted to see the Castle of Zenda and in half an hour I had climbed the hill to it. There were two buildings — the old one, with a moat around it, and the new, modern building. Duke Michael could have friends to stay with him in the new castle, but he could go into the old castle when he wanted to be alone. The water in the moat was deep, and if he pulled up the drawbridge over the moat, no one could get to him.

I stayed there for some time and looked at the castle, and then I walked on through the forest for about an hour. It was beautiful and I sat down to enjoy it. Before I knew what had happened, I was asleep.

Suddenly I heard a voice say, 'Good heavens! He looks just like the King!'

When I opened my eyes, there were two men in front of me. One of them came nearer.

'May I ask your name?' he said.

'Well, why don't you tell me your names first?' I replied.

The younger of the two men said, 'This is Captain Sapt, and

12

姑娘笑了起来。"是因为你的头发,先生。"她解释道。"我们在这儿不常见到这种颜色的头发。这是艾尔弗伯格家族的红色。这可不是约翰最喜欢的颜色。"

第二天,我决定步行数英里穿过森林,然后从路边的一个小站上火车去斯特莱索。我把行李交火车托运了。午饭后我开始步行。首先我想看看曾达的城堡。半小时后我爬到了城堡所在的山上。那儿有两幢建筑物,一旧一新,旧的被一道护城河所环绕,新的是一座现代的建筑。迈克尔公爵可以和朋友一起呆在新城堡里,但假如他想要一个人呆着,他可以去旧城堡。壕沟里的水很深,如果他拉起跨越壕沟的吊桥,没人能靠近他。

我在那儿呆了一会儿,看着城堡,然后我走了差不多一个小时穿过森林。森林很美,我坐下来欣赏。一会儿我就睡着了。

突然间我听到一个声音说:"天哪,他真像国王!"

我睁开眼睛,面前站着两个人,其中一个走近我。

"请问您尊姓大名?"

"可是,您干吗不先告诉我您的姓名呢?"我回答。

两人中年轻的一位说:"这位是萨普特

favourite n. something or someone that is loved above all others. 最喜爱的人或物. **decide** v. think about and come to a conclusion. 决定,下决心. **moat** n. deep, wide ditch filled with water, round a castle, etc., as a defence. 壕沟, 护城河. **drawbridge** n. bridge that can be pulled up at the end by chains. 活动桥,吊桥.

13

I am Fritz von Tarlenheim. We work for the King of Ruritania.'

'And I am Rudolf Rassendyll,' I answered, 'a traveller from England. My brother is Lord Burlesdon.'

'Of course! The hair!' Sapt cried. 'You know the story, Fritz?'

Just then a voice called out from the trees behind us. 'Fritz! Fritz! Where are you, man?'

'It's the King!' Fritz said, and Sapt laughed.

Then a young man jumped out from behind a tree. I gave a cry, and when he saw me, he stepped back in sudden surprise. The King of Ruritania looked just like Rudolf Rassendyll, and Rudolf Rassendyll looked just like the King!

For a moment the King said nothing, but then he asked, 'Captain... Fritz... who is this?'

Sapt went to the King and spoke quietly in his ear. The King's surprise changed slowly to an amused smile, then suddenly he began to laugh loudly. 'Well met, cousin!' he cried. 'Where are you travelling to?'

'To Strelsau, sir – to the coronation.'

The King looked at his friends, and, for a moment, he was serious. But then he began to laugh again. 'Wait until brother Michael sees that there are two of us!' he cried.

'Perhaps it isn't a very good idea for Mr Rassendyll to go to Strelsau,' Fritz said, worried, and Sapt agreed with him.

'Oh, we'll think about the coronation tomorrow,' the King

14

上尉,我是弗里茨·冯·塔伦汉姆。我们是卢里塔尼亚国王手下的。"

"我是鲁道夫·拉森狄尔,"我回答说,"我是从英国来的游客,我哥哥是伯利斯顿勋爵。"

"当然啦! 瞧那头发!"萨普特叫道,"你知道那个故事吧,弗里茨?"

正在这时,一个声音从我们背后的树林里传来:"弗里茨! 你在哪儿呢,伙计?"

"是国王。"弗里茨说。萨普特笑了。

然后一个年轻人从一棵树后面跳了出来,我叫了一声,当他看见我时,惊愕地后退了一步。卢里塔尼亚国王看上去正像鲁道夫·拉森狄尔,鲁道夫·拉森狄尔看上去正像卢里塔尼亚国王。

有一小会儿国王什么也没说,然后他问:"上尉……弗里茨……,这是谁?"

萨普特走上去对着他的耳朵轻轻说了几句,国王惊讶的表情慢慢变成了一个感到有趣的微笑。"幸会,表弟!"他突然高声叫道,"你打算去哪儿?"

"去斯特莱索,去看加冕典礼。"

国王看看他的朋友,严肃了一会儿。然后他又笑起来了,"等着吧,让迈克尔老弟看看我们有两个。"

"也许,拉森狄尔先生不应该去斯特莱索。"弗里茨担心地说。萨普特也同意他的看法。

"哦,我们明天再谈加冕的事吧。"国王

serious *adj*. solemn, *thoughtful*. 严肃的,认真的。

15

said. 'Tonight we'll enjoy ourselves. Come, cousin!'

We returned to the Duke's house in the forest, where we had an excellent dinner. The King called loudly for wine, and Captain Sapt and Fritz seemed worried. Clearly, the King liked his wine a little too much.

'Remember the coronation is tomorrow,' warned old Sapt.

But the King was only interested in enjoying himself tonight, so we all drank and talked, and drank again. At last the King put down his glass and said, 'I've drunk enough.'

As he said that, old Josef, the King's servant, came in. He put some very special old wine on the table in front of the King and said, 'Duke Michael offers you this wine and asks you to drink it for love of him.'

'Well done, Black Michael!' the King cried. 'Well, I'm not afraid to drink your wine!'

And he drank every drop of wine in the bottle, himself. Then his head fell forward on to the table, and soon afterwards I too remembered no more of that wild evening.

说,"今晚我们要好好乐一乐。来吧,表弟!"

我们回到公爵的林中住宅,在那儿吃了一顿非常不错的晚餐。国王嚷嚷着要酒,而上尉萨普特和弗里茨看上去很焦虑不安。很显然,国王过于喜欢喝酒了。

"记住,明天就加冕了。"老萨普特警告说。可是国王只对今晚让自己好好乐一乐感兴趣,所以我们都喝酒,说话,然后又喝酒。最后国王放下杯子说:"我已经喝得够多的了。"

这时,国王的仆人约瑟夫进来了,他把一瓶非常古老特别的酒放在国王面前的桌子上说道:"迈克尔公爵奉上这瓶酒,并请您为了他对您的爱而喝了它。"

"干得好,黑迈克尔!"国王叫道,"好吧,我才不怕喝你的酒呢!"

他一个人喝干了瓶里的最后一滴酒。然后他的头伏在了桌子上。很快我自己也记不清那个疯狂的夜晚发生的别的事情了。

excellent *adj. very good, of high quality.* 极好的,优秀的。

3

The King goes to his coronation

I do not know how long I was asleep, but when I woke up I was cold and wet. Sapt and Fritz stood there looking at me. 'We had to wake you,' Sapt said. 'Cold water was the only way.'

Fritz took my arm and turned me round. 'Look!' he said.

The King was on the floor, and when Sapt pushed him with his foot, he did not move.

'We've been trying to wake him for half an hour,' said Fritz. 'But he's sleeping like a dead man.'

The three of us looked at each other.

'Was there something in that last bottle of wine?' I asked.

'I don't know,' Sapt said, 'but if he doesn't get to his coronation today, there'll never be a coronation for him. All Ruritania is waiting for him in Strelsau and Black Michael with half the army, too. We can't tell them that the King is too drunk to go to his own coronation!'

'You can say he's ill,' I said.

'Ill!' Sapt laughed angrily. 'Everybody will know what that means. He's been "ill" too many times before.'

'Tell me, do you think somebody put something in his wine?' I asked.

'It was Black Michael!' Fritz replied. 'We all know he wants to be King himself.'

18

3 国王加冕

　　我不知道自己睡了多长时间，醒来时我发觉又冷又湿。萨普特和弗里茨站在那儿看我。"我们得弄醒你，"萨普特说，"凉水是唯一的办法。"

　　弗里茨抓住我的胳膊让我转过身："你看，"他说。

　　国王在地板上。萨普特用脚碰他，但是他不动。

　　"我们一直在想弄醒他，都有半个小时了。"弗里茨说，"可他睡得像死人一样。"

　　我们三人你看看我，我看看你。

　　"最后那瓶酒里有什么东西吧？"

　　"我不知道。"萨普特说，"不过假如他今天不去加冕，他就永远别想有另一个加冕典礼。所有的卢里塔尼亚人都在斯特莱索等着他。黑迈克尔也在那儿，还带着一半儿军队。我们没法告诉他们国王醉得太厉害，参加不了自己的加冕大典。"

　　"你可以说他病了。"我说。

　　"病了！"萨普特冷笑道，"谁都知道病了是什么意思。他以前已经病得太多了。"

　　"告诉我，你们想会不会有人把什么东西放在他的酒里了？"我问。

　　"是黑迈克尔干的！"弗里茨回答，"我们都知道他自己想当国王。"

push *v. use force to cause sb. or sth. to move forward. Contrasted to "pull". 推，挤，与"拉"相对。* **drunk** *adj. under the influence of alcohol. 醉的，喝醉了的。*

For a moment or two we were all silent, and then Sapt looked at me, 'You must go to Strelsau and take his place!'

I stared at him. 'You're crazy, man! How can I do that? The King...'

'It's dangerous, I know,' said Sapt. 'But it's our only chance. If you don't go, Black Michael will be King and the real king will be dead or a prisoner.'

How could I refuse? It took me two minutes to decide.

'I'll go!' I said.

'Well done, boy!' cried Sapt. He went on quickly and quietly. 'After the coronation they'll take us to the palace for the night. When we're alone, you and I will leave and ride back here to fetch the King. He'll be all right by then. I'll take him back to Strelsau and you must get out of the country as fast as you can.'

'But what about the soldiers?' Fritz asked. 'They're Duke Michael's men, and they're coming to take the King back to Strelsau for the coronation.'

'We'll go before the soldiers get here,' Sapt said, 'and we'll hide the King.'

He picked up the King in his arms and we opened the door. An old woman, Johann's mother, was standing there. She turned, without a word, and went back to the kitchen.

'Did she hear?' Fritz asked.

'Don't worry. I'll make sure she can't talk,' Sapt said, and he carried the King away.

有那么一会儿我们都没说话，然后萨普特看着我，"你必须去斯特莱索代替他。"

　　我紧紧盯着他，"你疯了！我怎么能干这个！国王他……"

　　"这很危险，我明白，"萨普特说，"但这是我们唯一的机会，要是你不去的话，黑迈克尔就会成为国王，而真正的国王就会死去或者成为一名囚徒。"

　　我怎么能拒绝呢？我想了两分钟就下了决心。

　　"我去！"我说。

　　"太好了，小伙子！"萨普特叫道。他快速而小声地说下去，"大典之后，他们会带我们去王宫过夜，等到就剩我们的时候，你和我骑马回来接国王。他那时就没事了。我会带他去斯特莱索，而你必须离开这个国家。"

　　"可是那些士兵怎么办？"弗里茨问，"他们是黑迈克尔的人，他们会前来带国王到斯特莱索去加冕。"

　　"士兵还没到达之前我们就走。"萨普特说，"而且我们还要把国王藏起来。"

　　他抱起国王，我们打开了门。一个老太太，约翰的妈妈，正站在门外。她转过身，一句话也没说就走回了厨房。

　　"她听到了吗？"弗里茨问。

　　"别担心，我会弄妥让她没法告诉别人的。"萨普特说着，把国王弄走了。

take one's place: to act in-stead of sb. 代替，取代。crazy adj. mad, ill in the mind. 疯，糊涂。dangerous adj. able to or likely to cause suffering, injury or loss of life. 危险的，可能引起危险的。fetch v. go for and bring back sb. or sth. 取来，接来。pick up: take hold of and lift. 捡起，拿起。make sure: find out or arrange for certain. 使确信，肯定。

When he returned, he told us that he had locked the old woman in a room underground. The King and Josef were hidden in another room underground. 'Josef will take care of the King and tell him everything when he wakes up. Come,' he went on, 'there's no time to lose. It's already six o'clock.'

Soon I was dressed in the King's clothes, the horses were ready and we were on our way. As we rode through the forest, Sapt told me everything that he could about my life, my family, my friends, and the things I liked or did not like. He told me what to do when we got there, and how to speak to different people. He was a wonderful teacher, and I listened hard. One mistake could mean death for all three of us.

It was eight o'clock when we arrived at the station and got on the train, and by half-past nine we were in Strelsau.

And when King Rudolf the Fifth stepped out of the train, the people shouted, 'God save the King!'

Old Sapt smiled, 'God save them both,' he said quietly. 'I only hope we are all alive tonight!'

等他回来时，他告诉我们，他已经把那个老太太锁在一间地下室里了。"约瑟夫会照顾国王的，等国王醒来时会把什么都告诉他。来吧，"他说，"没有时间了，已经 6 点了。"

　　很快，我穿上了国王的衣服，马早已备好，我们就上路了。当我们穿过森林时，萨普特尽他所能地告诉我一切，有关我的生活，我的家庭，我的朋友，我喜欢什么不喜欢什么。他告诉我等到了那儿要做什么，以及怎么和不同的人说话。他是个好老师，我听得也很努力，因为一个错误就可能让我们三人丧命。

　　我们到车站上车的时候是 8 点钟。8 点半我们就到了斯特莱索。

　　当国王鲁道夫五世迈出车厢时，人们欢呼道："上帝拯救国王！"

　　老萨普特微笑道，"上帝拯救他们两个人。"他小声说，"我只希望今晚我们都还活着！"

---

underground *adj*. *under the surface of the ground*. 地下的。 **take care of**: *look after*. 照顾，照料。 **hard** *adv*. *with great effort*. 努力地，尽力地。

$\underline{4}$
My adventures begin

As we made our way to the palace, I began to feel that I really was the King of Ruritania, with Marshal Strakencz, the head of the army, on my right and old Sapt on my left. I could see that Strelsau was really two towns – the Old Town and the New Town. The people of the Old Town, who were poor, wanted Duke Michael to be their King, but the people of the New Town wanted King Rudolf. We went through the New Town first, and it was bright and colourful, with the ladies' dresses and the red roses of the Elphbergs. The people shouted loudly for their King as we passed through the streets. But when we came to the Old Town, the Marshal and Sapt moved nearer to my horse, and I could see that they were afraid for me.

'Stay back!' I called. 'I'll show my people that I'm not afraid of them.' Some of the crowd were pleased when they heard this, but most of them watched me in silence.

Finally, we reached the great church of Strelsau. I remember very little of the coronation – only two faces. One was a beautiful girl with wonderful red hair, the Princess Flavia. The other was the face of a man with black hair and dark, deep eyes – Black Michael. When he saw me, his face turned white. Clearly, he was surprised and deeply unhappy to see me.

The coronation seemed to last for hours, but I managed to

24

4 我的历险开始了

在去王宫的路上，军队的首领斯特肯茨元帅站在我的右边，老萨普特站在我的左边，我开始感到自己真的是卢里塔尼亚的国王了。我看到斯特莱索实际上是两个城——老城和新城。老城的人是穷人，他们想要迈克尔公爵当国王。新城的人却希望鲁道夫当国王。我们先经过新城，城里女人们的衣饰和艾尔弗伯格红玫瑰使得城市明亮艳丽。我们经过大街时，人们高声为国王欢呼。但当我们来到老城时，元帅和老萨普特靠近我的马，我能看出他们为我担心。

"退回去！"我叫道："我要让我的人民看看我并不害怕他们。"人群中有些人听到了我的话感到很高兴，但大多数人沉默地看着我。

终于我们来到了斯特莱索大教堂，大典的事儿我差不多都记不得了，除了两张面孔以外。一张是一个漂亮姑娘的，她长了一头绝妙的红头发。她是弗蕾维亚公主。另一张脸是一个男人的，他长着黑头发，深黑色的眼睛。他就是黑迈克尔。当他看见我时，他的面色发白了。很清楚，他见到我很吃惊，而且非常不快。

加冕典礼持续了几个小时，但我总算说

adventure n. a journey, activity, etc. that is strange and exciting and often dangerous. 奇遇，冒险。**marshal** n. a very important army officer. 元帅。**the red roses of the Elphbergs**: a kind of rose. 一种玫瑰。**manage** v. to succeed in dealing with (a difficult movement or action). 完成，设法办成。

say and do all the right things. At last it was over, and I was now the King of Ruritania! As Princess Flavia and I drove back to the palace in an open car, one man in the crowd called out, 'When's the wedding?'

The Princess's face went a little pink when she heard this. After a while she said, 'You seem different today, Rudolf. Quieter and more serious. Are you going to become a more sensible person now?'

The Princess, I realized, did not think very highly of the King. As for me, I thought the King was a very lucky man.

'If that will please you, I'll try to do it,' I said softly.

The Princess's face went pink again. Then she said, 'You must be careful of Michael. You know – '

'I know,' I said, 'that he wants what I have, and also what I hope to have one day.' As I spoke, I looked at her, and she smiled at me prettily.

'I wonder what the King's doing now,' I thought.

*   *   *

The royal dinner went on for a long time, but at last Fritz, Sapt, and I were alone in the King's dressing-room.

'You did well,' Fritz said, 'but, Rassendyll, be careful! Black Michael looked blacker than ever today – because you and the Princess had so much to say to each other.'

'She's very beautiful,' I replied.

'Come on,' Sapt cried. 'There's no time for that now. We must leave for Zenda at once, to find the King! If we're

26

对了也做对了所有的事儿。最后仪式终于结束了，现在我是卢里塔尼亚国王了！当弗蕾维亚公主和我乘着敞篷车回宫殿时，人群中有人对我们喊道："什么时候举行婚礼？"

公主听到这话时她的脸有点儿发红。过了一会儿她说："鲁道夫，你看起来不大一样，你变得安静严肃了。你现在会变得更明智些了吧？"

我明白了，公主对国王的评价不太高。在我看来，国王是一个非常幸运的人。

"如果那样能使你高兴的话，我就试试这么做。"我柔和地说。

公主的脸红了，然后她说："你得小心迈克尔，你知道……"

"我知道，"我说，"他想得到我所拥有的，还想得到我有朝一日想得到的。"我这么说的时候眼睛看着她，她对我微笑着，很可爱。

"我真想知道国王现在在在干嘛？"我暗想。

宫廷晚宴持续了很长时间，不过弗里茨、萨普特和我总算单独呆在国王的更衣室里了。

"你干得不错，"弗里茨说，"但是拉森狄尔，小心一点！黑迈克尔今天看起来特别黑，因为你和公主两人有那么多可说的了。"

"她美极了。"我回答。

"得了，"萨普特说，"现在没工夫说这些了，我们得立即去曾达，去找国王！假如我们

wedding *n. marriage ceremony.* 婚礼，婚庆仪式。
sensible *adj. having or showing good sense, reasonable, practical.* 明智的，明理的，切合实际的。**think highly of sb. or sth.**: *have a good opinion of sb. or sth.* 对……评价高。**wonder** *v. wish to know, ask oneself.* 想知道，自忖。**dressing-room**: *a room where people get dressed or have themselves made up.* 化妆室，更衣室。

caught, we'll all be killed! Black Michael has had a letter from
Zenda, so perhaps he knows already. Don't unlock the door,
Fritz, while we're away, or you'll be a dead man. Say the King
must be left alone to rest. Now, come on. The horses are
ready.'

Fritz and I shook hands, then I covered my red hair and
most of my face. Sapt and I left the room by a secret door, and
we found ourselves outside, at the back of the palace gardens. A
man was waiting there with two horses.

Soon we left the town behind us, and we were out in the
country. We rode like the wind and by ten o'clock had come to
the edge of the forest of Zenda.

Suddenly Sapt stopped. 'Listen!' he said quietly. 'Horses
behind us! Quick! Get down! The castle's to the left,' he
continued. 'Our road's to the right.'

We hid in the thick trees, and we waited and watched. The
men came nearer. It was Black Michael and another man.
When they came to the two roads, they stopped.

'Which way?' the Duke asked.

'To the castle!' the other man cried. 'They'll know there
what's been happening.'

The Duke waited for a moment. 'To Zenda then!' he cried
finally, and the two men took the road to the left.

We waited for ten more minutes, and then we hurried on.

When we arrived at the house in the forest, we ran to the
underground rooms. The one where Sapt had locked up the old

28

被逮住了,我们都得死! 黑迈克尔收到了一封曾达来的信,所以他也许已经知道了。我们不在的时候你别开门,弗里茨,不然你会死的。你就说国王得一个人呆着休息。现在,走吧,马已经准备好了。"

弗里茨和我握握手,然后我挡上我的头发和大半个脸。萨普特和我从一个秘密的门出了房间,就到了宫殿的花园后面,一个人正牵着两匹马等着我们。

很快我们将城市抛在了身后,进入了乡间。我们骑着马像风一样快,10 点钟时我们已经来到了曾达的森林边。

突然萨普特停住了。"听!"他悄悄地说,"我们后面有马蹄声! 快! 下马! 去城堡走左边的路,我们的路是右边这条。"

我们躲在密密的树林里,等待着,注视着。那些人走近了,是黑迈克尔和另一个男人。当他们走到两条路口时,他们停住了。

"怎么走?"公爵问。

"去城堡!"另一个说,"他们会知道那儿出了什么事。"

公爵等了一会儿。"那就去曾达!"他终于说道。然后两人就朝左边的路走了。

我们又等了十多分钟,然后赶紧上路。

我们到达林中小屋,冲进地下室。萨普

the country: *land used for farming or left unused, land outside cities or towns.* 乡间,田野。be-tween us: *as the result of our combined efforts.* (我们两人)合力,共同。

29

woman was empty. She had escaped! The other room was locked. Sapt's face was white with fear. Between us, we broke down the door and ran in. I found a light and looked round the room. The servant Josef was on the floor — dead! I held up the light and looked in every corner of the room.

'The King isn't here!' I said.

特老太太的那间房间空了。她逃走了！另一间房子锁着。萨普特的脸因为紧张而发白。我俩砸开门冲了进去，我找到一盏灯，朝四周看去，老仆人约瑟夫躺在地板上死了。我举着灯，把房间的每一个角落都看遍了。

"国王不在这儿。"我说。

5

His Majesty returns to Strelsau

I t was one o'clock in the morning. For a few minutes we said nothing. Then Sapt cried, 'The Duke's men have taken the King prisoner!'

'Then we must get back and wake everyone in Strelsau!' I cried. 'We must catch Black Michael before he kills the King.'

'Who knows where the King is now?' Sapt answered. Then suddenly he began to laugh. 'But we've given Black Michael a problem,' he said. 'Yes, my boy. We'll go back to Strelsau. The King will be in his palace in Strelsau again tomorrow.'

'No!' I cried.

'Yes!' Sapt answered. 'It's the only way to help him. Go back and take his place for him.'

'But the Duke knows...'

'Yes, but he can't speak, can he? What can he say? "This man isn't the King because I've taken the real King prisoner and murdered his servant." Can he say that?'

'But people will soon realize I'm not the real King,' I said.

'Perhaps, perhaps not,' said Sapt. 'But we must have a King in Strelsau, or Michael will ride in tomorrow as the new King! Listen, boy, if you don't go back to Strelsau, they'll kill the King. And if you *do* go back, they *can't* kill the King. Because if they kill him, how can they ever say that

5 国王回到斯特莱索

　　此刻是凌晨一点钟。有几分钟的时间我们一句话也没说，然后萨普特叫道："公爵的人把国王关起来了！"

　　"我们必须回到斯特莱索，唤醒那儿的每一个人。"我说，"我们必须在黑迈克尔杀了国王之前抓住他。"

　　"谁又知道国王在哪儿呢？"萨普特回答。然后他突然笑了起来："不过我们已经给了黑迈克尔一个难题。"他说，"是的，我的孩子，我们回斯特莱索去。明天国王又会在斯特莱索的宫中的。"

　　"不！"我说。

　　"是的！"萨普特回答，"这是唯一能帮助他的方法。回去，替他去当国王。"

　　"可是公爵明白……"

　　"没错，但他没法说出来，对吗？他能说什么呢？'这个男人不是国王，因为我把真正的国王关进牢里，而且杀了他的仆人。'他难道能这么说吗？"

　　"可是人们很快就会知道我不是真正的国王。"我说。

　　"也许会，也许不会。"萨普特说。"但我们必须得有一个国王在斯特莱索，否则迈克尔明天就会奔去成为新国王。听着，孩子，如果你不回斯特莱索，他们就会杀掉国王。可是如果你回去了，他们就不能杀他，因为假如他们杀了他，他们怎么才能说明你不是

His/Her Majesty: *form used when speaking of a king or queen.* 国王陛下，女王陛下。间接提及时用。直接称呼时用 "*Your Majesty*"。

33

you're not the real King? Don't you see?' he cried. 'It's a dangerous game, but it gives us a chance of winning.'

It was a wild, hopeless plan, but I was young. I would never have the chance of an adventure like this again. 'Sapt, I'll try it,' I said.

'Good for you!' Sapt cried. 'But we must hurry! Look!'

He pulled me over to the door. The moon was low now, and there was not much light, but I could just see a small group of men on horses. They were Black Michael's men, probably coming to take the dead body of Josef away.

'We can't let them go without doing something,' I said, thinking of poor Josef.

'Right,' Sapt agreed. We ran out of the back of the house, and quickly got onto our horses. Silently, we waited in the darkness, and then we galloped round the house and straight into the group of men. Between us, we killed three of them, but a bullet hit my finger and it began to bleed.

We rode hard all night and it was about eight or nine o'clock in the morning when we reached Strelsau. Luckily, the streets were still empty. We arrived at the palace, went in, and got to the dressing-room. When we opened the door, Fritz was asleep, but he woke immediately. When he saw me, he fell to the ground and cried, 'Thank God, Your Majesty! You're safe!'

'Well done, boy!' Sapt shouted. 'We'll do it!'

Fritz stood up. He looked at me, up and down, down and up.

真正的国王？你难道不明白吗?"他说,"这是一场危险的游戏,不过它给了我们一次获胜的机会。"

这是一个疯狂无望的计划,但是那时我正年轻,我不可能再有这样的奇遇了。"萨普特,我试试。"我说。

"太棒了!"萨普特说。"可我们得快点儿,你看。"

他把我拖到门边。月亮现在低低的,没有什么光亮,但我恰好能看见一小群人骑在马上。他们是黑迈克尔的人,可能是来运走约瑟夫的尸体。

"我们不能就这么让他们走了。"我说,心里想着可怜的约瑟夫。

"好吧。"萨普特同意了。我们从屋子背后跑出去,很快地骑上了马。在黑暗中我们悄悄地等着,然后飞快地绕过房子,直冲进那群人中。我们杀了他们三个人,不过有一枪打中了我的手指,手指流血了。

我们骑着马整整走了一夜,到达斯特莱索是早上八九点钟,幸运的是,街上还是空空的。我们到达王宫,走进去直到更衣室。当我们开开门时,弗里茨正在熟睡,但他立刻就醒来了。当他看见我时,他跪倒在地叫道:"感谢上帝,陛下,您平安无事!"

"干得好,孩子!"萨普特说,"我们就这么办。"

弗里茨站了起来,他看着我,从上到下,

wild *adj.* *having or showing lack of consideration or reflection.* 鲁莽的,轻率的。**good for you**: *well done.* 干得好(表示夸奖、赞美等)。**body** *n.* *corpse.* 死尸,尸体。**gallope** *v.* *to go at the fastest speed (on a horse).* 骑马疾驰,飞奔。**bullet** *n.* *a type of shot fired from a gun.* 枪弹,子弹。**bleed** *v.* *to lose blood.* 流血。**immediately** *adv.* *at once, without delay.* 立即,立刻。

35

Then he took a step backwards. 'Where's the King?' he cried.

'Be quiet,' Sapt warned him. 'Someone will hear!'

Fritz's face was white now. 'Is the King dead?' he asked quietly.

'Please God, no,' I answered. 'But Black Michael has him.'

*　　　*　　　*

The next day was a long one for me. Sapt talked to me for three hours about what I must do and what I must say, what I liked and what I didn't like. Then I had to do some of the King's business, but, because of my damaged finger, I did not have to write my name on any papers.

When, at last, I was alone with Sapt and Fritz, we began to talk about Black Michael. Fritz told me that Black Michael had six very dangerous men among his servants — three Ruritanians, a Belgian, a Frenchman, and an Englishman. They did anything that the Duke ordered, and did not stop at murder. Three of them — the foreigners, Fritz had heard — were in Strelsau now with Duke Michael.

Sapt banged the table with his hand in excitement. 'Then the King must be alive! Michael's brought the foreigners with him, and left the three Ruritanians to hold the King prisoner. Usually, the Six, as they're called, go everywhere with him.'

Fritz wanted to do something immediately about Black Michael and his men, but Sapt and I realized that we could not do anything openly.

'We'll play a waiting game, and let Michael make the first

36

从下到上。然后他后退一步:"国王在哪里?"他嚷道。

"安静点,"萨普特警告他,"别人会听见的。"

弗里茨的脸变白了,"国王死了吗?"他静静地问。

"上帝保佑吧,他还没有死。"我说,"不过黑迈克尔抓住他了。"

第二天对我来说十分漫长。萨普特对我说了三个小时,告诉我应该做什么,不能做什么,什么是我喜欢的,什么是我不喜欢的。接着我不得不做一些国王该做的事。不过,由于我的手伤了,我不用在任何纸上签名。

最后,当我又和萨普特、弗里茨在一起时,我们开始谈论黑迈克尔。弗里茨告诉我,黑迈克尔的随从中有六个非常危险的家伙,其中三个是卢里塔尼亚人,一个比利时人,一个法国人,还有一个英国人。黑迈克尔让他们做什么就做什么,就是杀人也干。弗里茨听说其中三个外国人现在正和黑迈克尔一起呆在斯特莱索。

萨普特兴奋地用手拍了一下桌子,"这么说国王肯定还活着。迈克尔带了三个外国人,让那三个卢里塔尼亚人看着国王。通常总是黑迈克尔走到哪儿他们六个跟到哪儿的。"

弗里茨想立即就对黑迈克尔和他的人采取行动,可萨普特和我觉得我们什么事也不能公开地干。

"我们要玩一场等待游戏,让迈克尔先

business *n*. *task*, *duty*, *what has to be done*. 职责, 该做的事。**damage** *v*. *cause harm or injury*. 损伤,损害。**murder** *n*. *unlawful killing of a human being on purpose*. 谋杀,杀害。**bang** *v*. *hit violently*. 猛击,敲打。

move, 'I said.

And so I continued as King of Ruritania. In order to help the real King, I tried to make myself popular with the people. I went riding through the streets, smiling and talking to everybody. I also went to visit the Princess Flavia. The King's officials had told me that the Princess was very popular, and the people hoped that she would become my wife.

It was easy for me to pretend to be in love with the Princess. Too easy. Those beautiful eyes and that lovely smile were stealing my heart. Here was my greatest danger! I was pretending to be another man, but losing my own heart. On my first visit, we sat together for a long time, talking of this and that. When I got up to leave, Princess Flavia said, 'Rudolf, you will be careful, won't you? You have enemies, as I'm sure you know, and your life is very important to . . . Ruritania. '

"Only to Ruritania?' I asked softly.

'And to your loving cousin, 'she answered quietly.

I could not speak. I took her hand in mine. Then, with a heavy heart, I left.

Of course, I made many mistakes in my new life as King. But I managed to talk my way out of them, with luck and with help from Fritz and Sapt. It was like living on a knife edge. Once I met my brother Michael in the Princess's house. We smiled and talked politely, but I could see the anger in his black eyes.

动手。"我说。

因此，我就继续当卢里塔尼亚的国王，为了帮助真正的国王，我试着得到人民的爱戴。我乘车穿过每条街道，对每个人微笑，跟每个人说话。我也去拜访弗蕾维亚公主。国王的官员们告诉我公主非常受百姓的欢迎，人们希望她会成为我的妻子。

对我来说，假装我正爱着公主是很容易的事儿，太容易了。她那美丽的眼睛和可爱的微笑正悄悄占据我的心。这才是我最大的危险！我假装是另外一个男人，但失去的是我自己的心。在我第一次拜访她的时候，我们在一起坐着，说这说那，过了很长时间。当我站起来告别的时候，弗蕾维亚公主说："鲁道夫，你会小心的，是吗？你有敌人，你肯定知道这个，而且你的生命对于卢里塔尼亚是很重要的。"

"只对卢里塔尼亚重要吗？"我温柔地问。

"对爱着你的表妹也一样。"她静静地回答。

我说不出话来。我握住了她的手，然后带着一颗沉重的心离开了她。

自然，在作为国王的新生活中，我犯了许多错误，但我很幸运，加上有弗里茨和萨普特的帮助，都设法掩饰过去了。这真像在刀刃上过日子。有一次我在公主的房子里遇见了我的兄弟迈克尔。我们微笑着，彬彬有礼地聊天，但我能看出他黑眼睛里的怒火。

pretend v. make oneself appear (to be sth., to be doing sth.), either in a play or to deceive others. 假装，伪装。

6
An adventure with a tea-table

One day Sapt brought me some news – he had found out where the King was. Duke Michael was holding him prisoner somewhere in the Castle of Zenda.

Sapt also brought me a letter. It was in a woman's handwriting.

'To know what you most wish to know,' the letter began, 'meet me tonight in the garden of the big house in New Avenue. Come at midnight, and come alone.'

There was another note on the back of the letter. 'Ask yourself which woman does not want Black Michael to marry the Princess. A. de M.'

'Antoinette de Mauban!' I cried. '*She* wants to marry the Duke.'

'That's true,' Sapt said. 'But you won't go, of course. They'll kill you! Duke Michael made her write this letter!'

'I must,' I replied. 'Every day we play this game there's more danger. I could make a mistake at any time, and, if I do, we'll all die. Don't you see? I have to go tonight. We can't go on much longer.'

'Then I'm coming too,' said Sapt.

So, at half-past eleven that night, Sapt and I rode out to the house in New Avenue. We left Fritz to watch my room in the palace. The night was dark, so I took a lamp. I also had my re-

40

6 茶桌历险

有一天萨普特带来了一个消息——他发现了国王在哪儿。迈克尔公爵把他关在曾达城堡里的什么地方。

萨普特还给我带来了一封信，是一个女人的笔迹。

"要想知道你最想知道的事，"这封信的开头这样写着，"请今晚去新马路大房子的花园见我。半夜12点，一个人来。"

信封的背面还有一句话："问问你自己哪个女人不想让你迈克尔和公主结婚。A. de M."

"安东纳特·德·莫班!"我叫了起来，"她想嫁给公爵。"

"确实如此。"萨普特说，"但是你可不能去。当然不行，他们会杀了你的! 是迈克尔公爵让她写这封信的!"

"我得去。"我说。"我们玩这场游戏，每过一天，危险就增加一分。我随时可能出错，而一出错我们就都完了。还不明白吗? 我今晚必须去。我们没法老这样继续下去。"

"那我也去。"萨普特说。

于是，那天晚上11点半，萨普特和我骑马去新马路的那所大房子。我们把弗里·茨留下来照应我在王宫中的屋子。夜很黑，我带了一盏灯。我还带了我的左轮手枪和一把刀。

handwriting *n.* (*person's style of*) *writing by hand.* 笔迹，书法。**midnight** *n.* *12 o'clock at night.* 午夜，半夜12点。**make sb. do sth.** : *force sb. to do sth.* 强迫，使某人做某事。**revolver** *n.* *a type of small gun (pistol).* 左轮手枪，转轮手枪。

volver and a knife.

We soon reached the house, and came to a gate in the wall. I got off my horse.

'I'll wait here,' said Sapt. 'If I hear anything, I'll –'

'Stay where you are!' I answered quickly. 'It's the King's only chance. They mustn't kill you too!'

'You're right,' said Sapt. 'Good luck!'

Silently, I opened the gate and went into the garden. In front of me I could see the dark shape of a summer-house and I moved towards it. Without a sound, I went up the steps, pushed open the door and went in. A woman hurried over to me and took me by the hand. I turned my lamp on her. She was beautiful.

'Close the door!' she said. 'We must be quick, Mr Rassendyll! Michael made me write the letter – three men are coming to kill you – three of the Six! They'll tell everyone that Sapt and Fritz von Tarlenheim murdered you. Then Michael will make himself King and marry the Princess.' Antoinette's beautiful eyes were sad as she added softly, 'I can't let him marry her. I love him!'

'But the King,' I said. 'I know he's in the Castle of Zenda – but where?'

'Go across the drawbridge and you come to a heavy door ... Listen! What's that? They're coming! They're too soon! Put out your lamp!' she cried, her eyes filled with fear. 'Quickly! You must go. There's a ladder at the end of the

42

很快我们来到那所大房子跟前。围墙中间有一座大门,我下了马。

"我在这儿等着。"萨普特说,"假如我听见什么动静,我就……"

"你就在这儿呆着!"我很快地回答,"这是国王唯一的机会。他们不会连你也一块杀的。"

"你说得对。"萨普特说,"祝你好运!"

我静悄悄地开了门,走进花园。我眼前能看见的是一所避暑别墅的昏暗轮廓。我朝它走去。我悄悄地走上台阶,推门进去。一个女人急步走过来拉住我的手。我用灯照着她,她很美。

"关上门!"她说。"我们得快一点,拉森狄尔先生。是迈克尔让我写这封信的,有三个人会来杀你——那六个人中的三个。他们会告诉每个人萨普特和弗里茨·冯·塔伦汉姆杀了你。然后迈克尔会登上王位,并且和公主结婚。"安冬纳特美丽的眼睛露出悲哀,低声说,"我不能让他娶她,我爱他。"

"我知道国王在曾达的城堡里,"我说,"但他在哪里?"

"过了吊桥你能看见一座厚重的大门……听!什么声儿?他们来啦!他们太快了!把灯灭了!"她说,眼睛里满是惊恐。"快点儿!你得走。花园尽头有一个梯子靠在墙上!"

shape *n. outer form, appearance of something that is seen.* 外形,轮廓。

43

garden, against the wall!'

But it was too late. The three men were already outside.
There was a small hole in the door, and I put my eye to it. My
hand was on my revolver. It was no good! There were three of
them. I could kill one perhaps, but then...

A voice came from outside. 'Mr Rassendyll...' It was the
Englishman. 'We only want to talk to you. Open the door.'

'We can talk through the door,' I replied. I looked through
the hole again and saw that they were on the top step. When I
opened the door, they would run at me.

'We'll let you go if you leave the country and we'll give
you fifty thousand English pounds,' continued Detchard, the
Englishman.

'Give me a minute to think,' I answered.

Wildly, I looked around the summer-house and saw a metal
garden table and some chairs. I picked up the table and held it
in front of me, by the legs. Then I went to the back of the
room and waited.

'All right, I agree,' I called. 'Open the door!'

I heard them arguing with each other, and then Detchard
said to the Belgian, 'Why, Bersonin, are you afraid of one
man?'

A second later the door opened.

De Gautet, the Frenchman, was with the other two, and the
three men were standing there with their revolvers ready. With
a shout, I ran at them as hard as I could. They tried to shoot

但是已经太晚了。那三个人已经来到屋外，门上有一个小洞，我从洞里向外看。我的手放在左轮手枪上。这不管用！他们有三个人，我也许能打中其中的一个，但是……

外面响起一个声音："拉森狄尔先生……"是那个英国人。"我们只是想跟你谈谈，开门。"

"我们可以隔着门谈。"我回答。我又从小洞往外看，见他们已经上到了最高一层的台阶。假如我开门，他们就会朝我扑过来。

"假如你离开这个国家，我们会让你走，而且会给你五万英镑。"戴查德，那个英国人说。

"让我想一想。"我回答。

慌乱中我朝房子四周扫了一眼，看见了一个金属的花园用的桌子和一些椅子。我抓着桌腿把它挡在身体前，然后退到房子的尽头等着。

"好吧，我同意了。"我高声说："开门吧！"

我听见他们互相吵嚷，然后戴查德对那个比利时人说："伯索宁，难道你还怕一个人吗？"

片刻之后，门就开了。

德·高蒂特，那个法国人和另外两个人在一起。他们三个端着上了镗的左轮手枪站在那儿。我大叫一声，用尽全力向他们冲

be no good: *be no use or of little use, of little value*. 没有用，不管用。**run at**: *attack suddenly*. 突然进攻，猛扑。**pound** *n*. *British unit of money*. 英镑，英国货币单位。**argue (with sb.)** *v*. *express disagreement, quarrel*. 争论，争吵。

me, but the bullets hit the table. The next second the table knocked them to the ground and we all fell on top of each other. Quickly, I picked myself up and ran for my life through the trees. I could hear them coming after me. Was Antoinette right? Was there really a ladder by the wall? I reached the end of the garden. The ladder was there! In a minute I was up it and over the wall.

Sapt was waiting with the horses and seconds later we were on our way home. And, as we rode, we laughed because I had fought Duke Michael's dangerous men – with a tea-table!

去。他们向我开枪,但是子弹打在了桌子上。紧接着桌子打倒了他们。我们都倒下了,你压着我,我压着你。很快我爬了起来,穿过树林飞快逃走。我听见他们追了上来。安冬纳特没说错吧?墙上真有一个梯子吗?我跑到了花园的尽头,梯子真的在那里!一刹那间我就登上了梯子越过了围墙。

萨普特牵着马在等我。几秒钟后我们就已经在回去的路上了。我们一边骑着马,一边大笑。因为我已经和迈克尔公爵的杀手斗了一场,而且只用了一张茶桌!

shoot v. to fire (a weapon). 开枪,射击。

47

7
For love of the King

E very day I was sent a secret report by the Chief of Police, and the next afternoon I was playing cards with Fritz when Sapt brought it in. We learned that Duke Michael and the Three had left Strelsau, and that Antoinette de Mauban had also left. Clearly, they had gone to Zenda. The report also said that the people were unhappy because the King had not yet asked Princess Flavia to marry him.

'Yes, 'said Fritz. 'It's true. I've heard that the Princess loves the King and she's very sad...'

'Well, 'Sapt informed us, 'I've arranged a dance at the royal palace this evening, for the Princess.'

'Why wasn't I told?' I asked angrily.

But Sapt continued, 'Everything is arranged. And tonight you must ask the Princess to marry you.'

'No! I'll do nothing to hurt her!' I cried.

'All right, my boy, 'Sapt smiled gently. 'Just say something nice to her, then. Remember, she thinks you're the King and we don't want her to be angry with him, do we?'

I understood, of course. If the King was saved, then Flavia must marry him. If he was not saved, then Sapt would ask me to stay and marry the Princess. Duke Michael must not be King.

The dance was wonderful. Flavia was beautiful and I danced

7 为了对国王的爱

第二天下午我和弗里茨打牌时,萨普特带给我一封密信,那时每天警察长都要给我送一份秘密报告。我们得知迈克尔公爵和他的三个杀手离开了斯特莱索,安冬纳特·德·莫班也走了。很明显,他们去了曾达。报告还说臣民不太高兴,因为国王还没有请求弗蕾维亚公主嫁给他。

"是这样,"弗里茨说,"这是真的,我听说公主爱国王,她很伤心……"

"喂,"萨普特通知我们,"我今晚在王宫为公主安排了一个舞会。"

"为什么事先不告诉我?"我生气地说。

可是萨普特继续说着:"一切都安排好了。今天你就向公主求婚。"

"不!我决不做任何伤害她的事!"我叫道。

"好的,我的孩子。"萨普特温和地微笑着。"那就只对她说些好听的话。记住,她以为你是国王。我们不想让她对国王生气,对吗?"

我当然明白,如果国王得救了,弗蕾维亚就必须跟他结婚,如果他没得救,萨普特就会请我留下来,并且娶弗蕾维亚公主。决不能让迈克尔公爵当国王。

舞会好极了。弗蕾维亚很美丽。我跟

chief *n. leader or ruler.* 头目,首领。 **inform** *v. to tell, give knowledge to sb. of sth.* 通知,报告,提供消息。 **arrange** *v. make plans in advance, see to the details of sth.* 安排。

with her again and again. Everyone could feel our happiness. I forgot about the crowd of rich, colourful people who were watching us. I had eyes only for my beautiful Flavia.

When supper had finished, Fritz touched me on the shoulder. I stood up, took Flavia's hand and led her into a little room. They brought coffee to us and then the door was closed quietly. The Princess and I were alone.

The windows of the little room opened onto the garden. The night was fine and the room was filled with the sweet smell of the flowers outside. Flavia sat down and I stood opposite her. I was fighting with myself...But then she looked at me – and I was lost! I forgot the King, I forgot who I was, I forgot everything! I fell to my knees, took her gently in my arms and kissed her.

Suddenly she pushed me away. 'Is it true? Do you really love me?' she cried. 'Or is it because you're the King and you must marry me?'

'No!' I answered quietly. 'I love you more than my life!'

Flavia smiled. 'Oh, why do I love you now?' she said softly. 'I didn't love you before, but I do now.'

How happy I was! It was not the King she loved. It was me – it was Rudolf Rassendyll! But as I looked into her lovely face, I knew I could not live with the lie. How could I pretend to be the King any longer?

'There's something I must tell you...' I began in a low voice.

她一遍又一遍地跳舞,每个人都能感到我们的快乐。我忘了那些有钱的,打扮得多姿多彩的人们在看着我们。我的眼里只有我美丽的弗蕾维亚。

晚餐结束后,弗里茨碰了碰我的肩膀,我站了起来,拉着弗蕾维亚的手,把她带进一个小房间里,他们给我们送来了咖啡,然后门就轻轻关上了,公主和我单独呆在一起。

小房间的窗户朝花园开着,夜色明朗,屋内充满了窗外鲜花的甜香。弗蕾维亚坐了下来,我站在她的对面。我跟自己在斗争着……可是她看着我,我失败了。我忘了国王,忘了我是谁,忘了一切。我跪了下来,轻轻地搂住她,吻了她。

突然她推开了我:"这是真的吗? 你真的爱我吗?"她说,"还是因为你是国王而不得不娶我?"

"不!"我静静地回答:"我爱你胜过爱我的生命!"

弗蕾维亚微笑了:"哦,为什么我现在爱你了?"她温柔地说,"以前我并不爱你,可现在我爱了。"

我多么幸福啊! 她爱的并不是国王,而是我——鲁道夫·拉森狄尔! 可是当我望着她可爱的脸,我知道我没法再对她撒谎。我怎么能继续装扮我是国王呢?

"有件事我必须告诉你……"我低声说。

touch v. to feel with hands or fingers. 触摸,抚摸。shoulder n. the top of the arm where it joins the body. 肩膀。opposite prep. facing. 对面,与……相对。

51

'Your Majesty,' said a voice from the garden. 'People are waiting to say goodbye.'

It was Sapt. He had heard me talking to the Princess.

'We'll come,' I replied coldly.

But Flavia, her eyes full of her love for me, held out her hand to Sapt as he came into the room. He took it and said softly and sadly, 'God save your Royal Highness.' And then he added, 'But before all comes the King – God save the King!'

When Sapt told the people that Princess Flavia had accepted the King as her future husband, they were wild with happiness.

'You know, Sapt,' I said sadly, 'I could marry the Princess and let my people kill Duke Michael – and the King.'

'I know,' Sapt replied quietly.

'So we must go to Zenda and bring the King home at once!' I said.

Sapt put his hand on my shoulder. 'You're the finest Elphberg of them all,' he said with feeling.

*　　　　*　　　　*

Before we left Strelsau, I saw the Marshal and asked him to stay near Flavia, to take care of her and to keep her safe from Duke Michael. Then I went to say goodbye to her. At first she was cold with me. She did not understand why I wanted to leave her. But her anger changed to fear when I told her that I was going after Duke Michael.

'Oh, Rudolf, be careful!' she cried. 'He's a dangerous man!

52

"国王陛下，"花园里有人说道："人们都在等着跟您告别呢。"

是萨普特，他听见我和公主说的话了。

"我们就来。"我冷冷地回答。

可是弗蕾维亚的眼里充满了对我的爱，对走进房间的萨普特伸出手去。他握着她的手，温柔而又伤感地说："上帝拯救公主殿下。"然后他又加了一句："可是国王高于一切，上帝拯救国王！"

当萨普特宣告说弗蕾维亚公主接受国王作为她未来的丈夫时，人们都乐得发疯了。

"你知道，萨普特，"我悲哀地说，"我可以娶了公主，并且让我的人民杀了迈克尔公爵，还有国王。"

"我知道。"萨普特静静地回答。

"所以我们必须立即去曾达，把国王弄回来！"

萨普特把手放在我的肩上："在所有艾尔弗伯格家族的人当中，你是最好的一个。"他动情地说。

在我们离开斯特莱索之前，我见了元帅，并且请他呆在弗蕾维亚身边，照顾她并且使她免受迈克尔公爵的打扰。然后我去向她告别。起初她对我很冷淡，她不明白为什么我想离开她。但当我告诉她我去追赶迈克尔公爵时，她的怒气变成了恐惧。

"哦，鲁道夫，小心点儿！"她说，"他是个

Your Royal Highness: *title used when speaking to a certain royal person*. 对王室成员的称呼，殿下。**accept** *v. to take or receive willingly*. 接受，收下。

53

Please come back safely to me. '

  ' Duke Michael can never keep me away from you, ' I promised. But in my heart I knew that another man could.

危险的家伙！请你一定要平安地回到我的
身边。"

　　"迈克尔公爵永远也别想让我离开你。"
我保证道。但在我心里，我知道另一个人却
能做到。

8

Back to Zenda

The next day Sapt, Fritz, and I left Strelsau to go to
Tarlenheim House. This fine modern house belonged
to Fritz's uncle and was near the Castle of Zenda. We had ten
brave young men with us. Sapt had told them that a friend of
the King's was a prisoner in the Castle of Zenda and that the
King needed their help.

Michael, of course, knew of my arrival. But I was sure he did
not understand why I had come. He would think that my plan
was to kill him *and* the King — and marry the Princess myself.
So, I had not been in the house an hour when he sent three of
the Six to me. These were not the three men who had tried to
kill me. This time he sent the three Ruritanians — Lauengram,
Krafstein and young Rupert of Hentzau.

'Duke Michael is very sorry that he can't welcome you himself,' explained Rupert of Hentzau. 'But, sadly, he's ill at the
moment.'

'I hope that my dear brother will soon be better,' I replied
with a smile.

Rupert threw back his head, shook his black hair and
laughed. He was a good-looking young man. People said he had
broken many hearts already.

'Oh, I'm sure he will!' he answered.

8 回到曾达

第二天萨普特、弗里茨和我离开斯特莱索去塔伦汉姆庄园。这所新式的庄园属于弗里茨的叔叔，离曾达城堡不远。我们带了10个勇敢的年轻人。萨普特告诉他们说，国王的一个朋友被关在曾达的城堡里了，国王需要他们的帮助。

迈克尔当然知道我来了，可是他肯定不明白为什么我要来。他会以为我的计划是把他和国王都杀了。然后我自己和公主结婚。因此，我到庄园还不到一个小时，他就派了那六个人中的三个来见我。他们不是曾经追杀我的那三个人。这一次他派了三个卢里塔尼亚人——劳恩格兰姆，克拉夫斯坦，和年轻的亨佐鲁帕特。

"迈克尔公爵很抱歉他不能亲自来欢迎您。"鲁帕特解释说，"很遗憾，他现在病了。"

"我希望我亲爱的兄弟很快会好起来。"我微笑着回答。

鲁帕特一仰头，甩了甩他的黑头发也笑了。他长得很精神，据说他已经让很多女人心碎了。

"哈，我肯定他会好起来的!"他回答。

modern *adj. new and up-to-date.* 新式的，时髦的。
arrival *n. act of reaching a place, esp. the end of a journey.* 到达，到来。
break one's heart: *make sb. very sad.* 令人心碎，使人伤心。

57

*   *   *

That evening, instead of having dinner at the house, Fritz and I went to the little hotel in the town of Zenda where I had stayed before.

'Ask for a room where we can dine alone,' I said to Fritz. 'And ask the pretty girl to bring our food.'

I covered my face and the girl came and put the wine down on the table. When she turned to go, she looked at me and I let her see my face.

'The King!' she cried. 'You were the King! Oh, I'm sorry, sir! I'm sorry! The things that we said!'

'Forget that now,' I answered. 'You can help me. Bring our dinner, but tell no one that the King is here.'

She came back in a few minutes, looking very serious.

'How's your friend Johann?' I began.

She looked surprised. 'Oh, we don't see him very often now,' she answered. 'He's very busy at the castle.'

'But you could get Johann to meet you tomorrow night, couldn't you? At ten o'clock, perhaps, on the road out of Zenda.'

'Yes, sir... You're not going to hurt him?'

'Not if he does what I say. Go now, and say nothing about this.'

After dinner, we left to go back to Tarlenheim House. We had almost reached it when we saw Sapt running to meet us. 'Have you seen them?' he cried.

58

那天晚上, 弗里茨和我没在庄园里吃饭, 我们去了曾达城中我曾经住过的小旅店。

"你去要一个我们可以单独用餐的小房间," 我对弗里茨说, "还有, 请那个漂亮的姑娘给我们上吃的。"

我挡住我的脸。那姑娘进来把酒瓶放在桌上, 当她转身要走时, 她看着我, 我让她看见了我的脸。

"是国王!" 她叫道, "你是国王! 哦, 我很抱歉, 先生, 对不起, 我们说了那些话!"

"现在忘了那些。" 我回答, "你能帮我的忙。给我们把晚餐拿来, 不过别告诉任何人国王在这儿。"

几分钟后她回来了, 看上去非常严肃。

"你的朋友约翰他好吗?" 我问。

她看上去有点吃惊:"噢, 我近来不常见到他。" 她说, "他在城堡里很忙。"

"可你能叫约翰明天晚上跟你见面, 对吗? 大概晚上十点, 在曾达城外的路上。"

"是的, 先生, 你们不会伤害他吧?"

"如果他照我说的做就不会。现在去吧。对这事一个字也别说出去。"

吃完晚饭, 我们回到塔伦汉姆庄园。我们快到的时候, 看见萨普特跑出来迎接我们。"你们看见他们了吗?" 他问。

'Who?' I asked.

'Duke Michael's men. Don't go out unless you have six men or more with you!' he said. 'You know Bernenstein, one of your men?'

'Of course,' I answered. 'A good, strong man, about as tall as me.'

'Well, they tried to kill him. He's upstairs now with a bullet in his arm. He was walking in the woods and he saw three men. Suddenly, they started shooting at him, so he began to run. He was lucky. They were afraid to come too near the house, so he escaped. But it was you they wanted to kill!'

'Sapt,' I said, 'I promise I'll do one thing for Ruritania before I leave it.'

'What's that?' asked Sapt.

'I'll kill every one of the Six. Ruritania will be a better place without them!'

"谁?"

"迈克尔公爵的人。如果你身边没有六个人或更多的人,就别到外边去!"他说:"你知道伯南斯坦吧? 他也是你的人。"

"当然啦。"我回答,"他人好,又强壮,差不多跟我一样高。"

"嗯,他们想杀了他。他现在在楼上,胳膊上中了一枪。他在树林散步的时候看见三个人,突然他们向他开枪,他就跑。他很幸运。他们不敢太靠近这所房子,所以他侥幸逃脱了。可是他们想杀的是你!"

"萨普特,"我说,"我保证在我离开卢里塔尼亚之前要做一件事。"

"什么?"萨普特问。

"我要干掉那六个人中的每一个。没有了他们,卢里塔尼亚会更好!"

---

upstairs *adv.* *to or on a higher floor.* 楼上。

$$9$$

News of the prisoner

T he next morning I was sitting in the garden in the sun when suddenly I saw young Rupert of Hentzau on horseback coming through the trees towards me. He was not afraid of my men, but asked to speak with me alone. He said he had a message for me from the Duke of Strelsau. I asked my friends to move away, and Rupert came and sat down near me.

'Rassendyll,' he began, 'the Duke...'

'Don't you know how to speak to the King?' I asked.

'Why pretend with me?'

'Because it isn't finished yet.'

'Well, I'm here because I want to help you...'

'Then give me the message. What does the Duke want?' I asked.

'He wants you to leave. He'll take you safely out of the country and give you a hundred thousand pounds.'

'I refuse,' I replied immediately.

Rupert laughed. 'I knew it!' he cried. 'Duke Michael doesn't understand men like us!... You must die, then,' he added carelessly.

'Yes,' I answered. 'But you won't be alive to see me die!' I laughed. 'How's your prisoner?' I added.

'Alive,' he replied. 'How's the pretty Princess?'

I took a step towards him. 'Go now, before I kill you,' I

9 有关囚犯的消息

第二天早晨,我正坐在阳光下的花园里,突然看见鲁帕特骑着马穿过树林朝我走来。他并不怕我的人,但是请求和我单独谈谈。他说他有斯特莱索公爵给我的口信。我请朋友们离开,然后鲁帕特过来在我旁边坐了下来。

"拉森狄尔,"他开始说,"公爵……"

"难道你不知道应该怎样对国王说话吗?"我问。

"干吗跟我装假?"

"因为事情还没完。"

"好吧,我来这儿是因为我想帮助你……"

"那就告诉我那个口信。公爵想要什么?"

"他要你离开。他会帮你安全地离开这个国家。而且会给你10万英镑。"

"我拒绝。"我立即回答。

鲁帕特笑了:"我知道,"他说:"迈克尔公爵不了解你我这样的人!……那么你就得死。"他漫不经心地加了一句。

"对。"我回答:"不过你也别想活着看到我死!"我笑着说:"你的犯人怎么样了?"

"还活着!"他回答:"美丽的公主怎么样了?"

我朝他跨了一步,"在我杀了你之前赶紧滚!"我生气地喊道。

message *n.* *piece of news, or a request, sent to sb.* 讯息,口信。**carelessly** *adv. done without care, thoughtlessly.* 粗心地,不在乎地。

63

shouted angrily.

Rupert turned, but suddenly he came back. He put out his right hand. 'Shake hands! ' he called.

Of course, he knew what I would do. I put my hands behind my back. Quickly, his left hand moved towards me. In it he held a dagger and it was coming straight at my heart! I jumped to one side, and the dagger went deep into my shoulder. Before my friends could do anything, Rupert of Hentzau was on his horse and galloping through the trees. I heard my men going after him with their guns – and then everything went black.

When I awoke it was dark, and Fritz was at my bedside. He told me that I was not badly hurt, and that the plan to catch Johann had been successful.

'He seems pleased to be here, ' Fritz said. 'I think he's afraid of Duke Michael. '

Later Sapt brought Johann up to see me. At first Johann was afraid to speak, but then he began to talk. We asked him many questions, and finally Johann gave us the information we wanted.

In the Castle of Zenda, near the drawbridge and below the ground, there were two small rooms, cut out of the rock itself. In the first of these rooms there were always three of the Six. At the back of this room there was a door which led into the second room. The King was in the second room.

'If someone tries to get into the first room, two of the three

鲁帕特转过身,但他突然又回来了。他伸出右手,叫道:"握握手吧!"

　　他当然知道我会怎么做。我把手放在背后。他的左手却一下子伸过来,手里的短剑直刺向我的心脏。我跳向一边,短剑深深地刺进我的肩膀。没等我的朋友反应过来,鲁帕特已经上马跑进了树林。我听见我的人开枪追赶他,然后一切都变黑了。

　　我醒来时天已经黑了。弗里茨坐在我的床边。他说我的伤不重,并且告诉我我们抓约翰的计划已经成功了。

　　"他看上去很高兴能呆在这儿。"弗里茨说,"我想他害怕迈克尔公爵。"

　　过了一会儿萨普特带约翰来见我。一开始约翰不敢说话,然后他开始说了。我们问了他许多问题,最后约翰终于把我们想知道的说了出来。

　　在城堡靠近吊桥的地方,有两个地下小屋,是从岩石中凿出来的。那六个人中的三个总是在第一间小屋里呆着,屋子的尽头安着一扇门通向第二间屋子,国王就在那里面。

　　"假如有人想进第一间屋子,那三个人

dagger *n*. *short*, *pointed*, *two-edged knife as a weapon*. 短剑,匕首。
pleased *adj*. *glad*, *feeling or showing satisfaction*. 高兴的,满意的。**information** *n*. *sth. told*, *news or knowledge given*. 消息,情报。

men will fight, but Rupert of Hentzau or Detchard will run into the second room and kill the King,' Johann said. 'There's a small window in the second room with a large pipe going down into the moat outside,' he went on. 'You can get a man inside it, and they'll tie a heavy stone to the King's body and push it down the pipe. The body will go down and disappear under the water, and the murderers will then go down the pipe themselves, and swim across the moat.'

'And if I bring an army to the castle?' I asked.

'Duke Michael will still murder the King,' replied Johann. 'He won't fight. He'll kill the King and push his body down the pipe. And he'll put one of the Six in the prison. He'll say the man had done something to make him angry. That will stop the stories about a prisoner in Zenda.' Johann stopped for a minute, but then he added, 'If they know I've told you this, they'll kill me. They're all bad, but Rupert of Hentzau is the worst. Don't let them kill me...'

'All right,' I said. 'But if anyone asks you who the prisoner of Zenda is, don't tell him. If you do, I'll kill you myself!'

Johann left the room and I looked at Sapt.

'It doesn't matter what plan we make,' I said. 'The King will be dead before we can get to him!'

Sapt shook his grey head angrily. 'You'll still be King of Ruritania in a year's time.'

'Perhaps one of the Duke's men will turn against him...' I began.

中的两人就会应战,而鲁帕特或者戴查德就会冲进第二间屋子把国王杀掉。"约翰说:"第二间屋子里有一个小窗子,一根大排水管穿过窗户通往外面的护城河。"他接着说,"排水管能容纳下一个人。他们会在国王身上绑上一块很重的石头,然后把他推下排水管。尸体掉下去,消失在水下,然后杀人犯们也会顺着排水管下来,再游泳穿过护城河。"

"假如我带领一支军队去攻打城堡呢?"我问。

"迈克尔公爵仍然会杀了国王,"约翰说。"他不会跟你硬打的。他会把国王杀了,推下排水管,然后把那六个家伙中的一个关进监狱。他会说那个家伙做了让他生气的事儿。这样就可以制止人们关于曾达有个囚徒的传言。"约翰停了一会儿,又说:"如果他们知道我告诉了你们这个,他们会杀了我。他们都很坏,可是最坏的是鲁帕特。别让他们杀了我……"

"好吧!"我说,"但如果有人问你曾达的囚徒是谁,你别说出来,不然的话我会杀了你!"

约翰离开了房间。我望着萨普特。

"我们订什么计划都无关紧要了。"我说,"还没等我们到国王身边他就已经死了。"

萨普特愤怒地摇着他灰白的脑袋:"一年之内你照样还是卢里塔尼亚的国王。"

"也许公爵的人里面会有一个起来反叛他……"我说。

pipe *n. tube used for carrying liquids or gas.* 管子,管道。**disappear** *v. to go out of sight, become lost.* 消失,失踪。**turn against sb.**: *become hostile to sb.* 变为敌对的态度,反抗。

'Impossible,' replied Sapt.

'Then we need the help of God,' I said.

"不可能。"萨普特回答。

　　"那我们就需要上帝来帮忙了。"我回答。

10
A night outside the castle

I wanted Duke Michael to think that I was still very ill, so we told the newspapers that the King had had a very serious accident. When Princess Flavia read this, she was very worried and she decided to come and see me. The Marshal could not stop her, and, although I was afraid for her, I was excited at the thought of seeing her again. We spent two wonderfully happy days together.

We had sent Johann back to the Castle of Zenda and suddenly we had a message from him. The real King was very ill.

'I must save him,' I said to myself. 'I love Flavia more each day. I can't go on like this much longer.'

I talked to Sapt. He agreed, so we made our plans.

*　　　　*　　　　*

Late the next night, Sapt, Fritz, and I, with six more men, rode out towards the Castle of Zenda. Sapt was carrying a long rope and I had a short, thick stick and a long knife.

The night was dark, and it was wet and windy. We stayed away from the town and we met no one. When we came to the moat, we stopped near some trees and the six men hid there with the horses. Then Sapt tied the rope round one of the trees near the water. I pulled off my boots, put the stick between my teeth and gently went down the rope into the water. I was going to take a look at the pipe.

10 城堡外的一夜

　　我想让迈克尔公爵以为我还十分虚弱，所以我们在报纸上说国王出了很严重的意外事故。当弗蕾维亚公主看到这条消息时，她非常忧虑，决定前来看我。元帅阻止不了她。虽然我替她担心，但也很高兴能再见到她。我们在一起过了幸福的两天。

　　我们派约翰回曾达的城堡去了。突然，我们得到了他传来的一个消息：真正的国王病得很重。

　　"我得救他。"我对自己说，"我对弗蕾维亚的爱每天都在增加，我没法儿再这样继续下去了。"

　　我和萨普特谈了我的想法，他同意了。我们就决定了行动计划。

　　第二天深夜，萨普特、弗里茨和我，还有另外六个人，骑马向曾达城堡进发。萨普特带着一根长绳，我拿着一根又短又粗的棍子和一把长刀。

　　夜色很黑，空气潮湿。我们绕开城市前进，没有撞上什么人。我们来到护城河的附近，在树丛里停了下来，那六个人和我们的马藏在里面。然后萨普特把绳子系在水边的树上，我脱下靴子，用牙咬着棍子，轻轻地顺着绳子下到河里，我要去看一下那根排水管。

accident *n. something esp. something unpleasant, undesirable, or damaging, that happens unexpectedly or by chance.* 意外，不测，祸事。**excite** *v. to cause sb. to lose calmness and to have strong feelings, often pleasant.* 使兴奋，激动。**gently** *adv. in a mild and careful way.* 温和地，轻轻地。

71

It had been warm and bright that day, and the water was not cold. Slowly and carefully I swam round the dark walls of the castle. There were lights in the new buildings, and from time to time I heard people shouting and laughing. 'That must be young Rupert and his friends,' I thought. Suddenly a dark shape appeared in front of me. It was the pipe! The bottom of it was very wide and came out into the moat. And then I saw something which nearly made my heart stop. It was a boat, and in the boat there was a man! His gun was beside him, but, luckily, he was asleep. As quietly as I could, I moved closer. The man still slept. What could I do? I had to save the King. I took out my knife and drove it through the sleeping man's heart! On the other side of the castle they were still singing.

I had very little time. Someone could come at any minute. I looked up at where the pipe went through the wall into the prison. There was a thin line of light at the bottom edge. I heard Detchard's voice, and then I heard the King reply. Just then the light went out, and, in the darkness, I heard the King crying. I did not call to him. I had to get away safely – and take the body of the dead watchman with me.

I climbed into the boat and began to go back to where my friends were. No one could hear me because the wind was strong. But from somewhere behind me, I heard a shout. Someone was calling to the watchman. I reached the side of the moat where Sapt and Fritz were waiting. Quickly, I tied the rope round the man's body and Sapt and Fritz pulled it up. Then I

那天很暖和,水也不冷。我缓慢而小心地绕着黑暗的城墙游着。城堡的新楼里有灯光,我不时能听见人们的叫声和笑声。"这一定是年轻的鲁帕特和他的同伙们。"我想。突然,一个黑影子出现在我的面前,是那根排水管!它的底部非常宽,伸进护城河里。然后我见到一样东西,我的心脏都几乎停止了跳动。是一只船,而且船里有个人!他的枪就靠在身边。幸运的是,他睡着了。我尽量轻轻地靠近他,他还在睡。我能怎么办呢?我得救出国王。我抽出刀,刺进了他的心脏。在城堡的另一边,那些人还在唱歌。

我的时间很紧,随时可能有人会来,我看了看排水管穿过城墙进入监狱的地方,在那个地方的底端有一丝光亮透了出来。我听见了戴查德的声音。然后我听见了国王的回答。就在这时灯光灭了。在黑暗中我听到了国王的哭声。我没叫他。我必须安全地离开,而且得带上那个死去的哨兵。

我爬进小船,开始往朋友们所在的地方划,没人能听见,因为风很大。但从我的背后,我听见一声叫唤,有人正在叫那个哨兵。我到了河边,萨普特和弗里茨正在等我。我很快地把绳子绕在那个哨兵的身上,他们把他拖了上去。然后我也顺着绳子爬了上去。

appear v. come into view, become visible. 出现, 呈现。 **bottom** n. lowest part of anything, inside or outside. 底部, 底端。

climbed up the rope myself.

'Call our men from the trees,' I said quietly. 'And hurry!'

But just then, three men rode round from the front of the castle. Luckily, they did not see us, but they heard our six friends riding out of the trees, and with a shout they galloped towards them.

Seconds later we heard the sound of shots and I ran to help our men. Sapt and Fritz followed.

'Kill them!' cried a voice. It was Rupert of Hentzau.

'Too late! They've got both of us!' cried another voice. 'Save yourself, Rupert!'

I ran on, holding my stick in my hand. Suddenly, through the darkness, I saw a horse coming towards me. I jumped at the horse's head, and saw the man's face above me.

'At last!' I shouted. 'Rupert of Hentzau!'

He had only his sword, and my men were coming at him from one side, and Sapt and Fritz from the other.

Rupert laughed. 'It's the play-actor!' he cried, and with his sword he knocked my stick from my hand. Then he turned his horse, galloped to the moat, and jumped into the water with our bullets flying round his ears. Our men tried to shoot him in the water, but it was dark, there was no moon – and we lost him.

We had killed two of the Six – Lauengram and Krafstein – but I was angry. Three of our brave friends were also dead, and we carried them home with a heavy heart.

"把我们的人叫来，"我悄声说。"要快！"

可就在此时，从城堡正面过来了三个骑马的人，很幸运他们没有看见我们，但他们听见了我们的六个朋友骑马从树林里出来，于是叫喊着扑向他们。

数秒钟后我们听见了枪声，我冲去帮助我们的人，萨普特和弗里茨紧跟着。

"杀死他们！"一个声音叫着，是亨佐的鲁帕特。

"太迟了，他们把我俩都抓住了，"另一个声音叫道："快逃吧，鲁帕特！"

我跑着，手里拿着棍子。突然，透过黑暗我看见一匹马向我这边冲来，我跳到了马头前，看见了我头顶上方那个人的脸。

"总算见面了！"我叫道："亨佐的鲁帕特！"

他手里只有剑，我的人从一边向他靠近，萨普特和弗里茨从另一边向他靠近。

鲁帕特笑了。"原来是那位演员！"他叫道。他用剑打掉我的棍子，然后掉转马头，冲进了护城河。我们的子弹在他耳边飞舞，我们的人向水中射击，但天太黑了，没有月亮，他逃脱了。

我们杀死了那六个人中的两个——劳恩格兰姆和克拉夫斯坦，但我很生气，我们有三个勇敢的朋友死了，我们把他们的尸体带回去，心情很沉痛。

And I did not like to hear Rupert call me a play-actor.

*　　　　*　　　　*

Of course, Michael and I could not let the people know that we were enemies. So, in the daytime it was safe to be in the town of Zenda. One day, soon after our night outside the castle, Princess Flavia and I were riding through the town when we saw a group of people dressed in black going to the church. Rupert of Hentzau was with them, and when he saw us, he turned his horse and came towards us.

'It's the funeral of my dear friend, Lauengram,' he said, in answer to our question.

'I'm sorry your friend is dead,' I said to him.

'And I'm sorry, too,' Flavia added, her beautiful blue eyes sad.

Rupert looked at her and smiled. Then he turned and rode away. Although I was angry because he had smiled at Flavia, I went after him.

'You fought bravely the other night,' I said, 'and you're young. Help me save the King – and I'll help you.'

But Rupert was not interested. 'No,' he answered. 'But if they were both dead – the King and the Duke – then you could be King and marry your Princess, and I could be rich, and have the woman I want.'

'Antoinette de Mauban?' I asked carelessly, trying not to show my interest.

'Yes,' replied Rupert. 'I hate the Duke. She loves him, not

我讨厌鲁帕特管我叫"演员"。

当然，迈克尔和我不会让人们知道我们是对头，因此白天在曾达城里是安全的。有一天，城堡外的那一夜之后没多久，当我和弗蕾维亚公主骑着马在城里穿行时，看见一群人穿着黑衣服走进教堂。鲁帕特也和他们在一起。他看见我们，掉转马头冲我们走来。

"这是我的朋友劳恩格兰姆的葬礼。"他回答我们的问题说。

"你的朋友死了我很难过。"我对他说。

"我也很难过。"弗蕾维亚说，她那美丽的蓝眼睛变得悲哀了。

鲁帕特看着她，微笑了。然后他骑马离开了。虽然他对弗蕾维亚微笑使我生气，我还是追了上去。

"那天晚上你很勇敢。"我说，"而且你正年轻，帮助我救出国王——我也会帮助你的。"

但是鲁帕特不感兴趣。"不，"他回答。"不过如果他俩都死了——国王和公爵——你就能当上国王，娶你的公主，而我就可以有很多钱，而且得到我想要的女人。"

"安·德·莫班?"我满不在乎地问，试图装着不感兴趣的样子。

"对。"鲁帕特回答。"我恨公爵，她爱的

funeral *n.* *a ceremony of burying or burning a dead person*. 葬礼，丧葬仪式。

77

me! ' Angrily, he joined the funeral group again.

Strangely, when we returned home there was a message for me from Antoinette herself.

' I helped you once. Help me now. Save me from this terrible place! Save me from these murderers! '

I was sorry for her, but what could I do?

是他,不是我!"他气冲冲地又回到葬礼的人群中去了。

奇怪的是,当我们回家时,一张安冬纳特本人写来的纸条正等着我们。

"我曾经帮助过你,现在帮帮我。把我从这个可怕的地方救出去! 从这些杀人凶手中间救出去!"

我为她感到难过,但是我又能怎么样呢?

terrible *adj*. *causing great fear or horror*. 可怕的,极糟的。

79

11
A dangerous plan

O ne day Johann came to tell us that the King was now very sick, and that Antoinette de Mauban and a doctor were looking after him. But the Duke never left Rupert of Hentzau alone with Antoinette. I understood why, after what Rupert had told me. There were often angry voices in the castle these days, Johann told us.

Two of the Six were now dead, but there were always two men watching the King. The other two slept in a room above and would hear them if they called. Detchard and Bersonin watched by night; Rupert of Hentzau and De Gautet by day. The Duke's rooms were on the first floor, in the new buildings of the castle, and Antoinette's room was on the same floor. But at night the Duke locked the door of her room, and pulled up the drawbridge. He kept the key himself. Johann slept near the front door of the new castle with five other men — but they had no guns.

We could not wait any longer. 'Listen!' I said to Johann. 'I'll make you rich if you do what I say.' Johann agreed.

'You must take this note to Madame de Mauban,' I said, 'and tomorrow, at two o'clock in the morning, you must open the front door of the new castle. Tell the others that you need air, or something — and then escape.'

Johann was clearly afraid, but he seemed to understand. I explained my plan to Sapt and Fritz.

80

11 一个危险的计划

一天约翰来告诉我们，国王病得很重，安冬纳特和一个医生正在照顾他。但是公爵从来不让鲁帕特和安冬纳特单独呆在一起。我明白这是为什么，鲁帕特已经告诉我了。约翰告诉我们，城堡里最近常有愤怒的叫嚷声。

虽然"那六个"中的两个已经死了，可是总有两个人看着国王，另外两个睡在楼上的一间屋子里，一叫就能听见。戴查德和伯索宁夜里看守，鲁帕特和德·高蒂特白天看守。公爵的房间是在城堡里新楼的一层。安冬纳特的房间也在这一层。但是一到夜里，公爵就把她的房门锁上，把吊桥拉起来，他自己拿着钥匙。约翰和另外五个人睡在新楼的正门附近，不过他们都没有枪。

我们不能再等了。"听着！"我对约翰说："我会让你发财，假如你照我的吩咐去做的话。"他同意了。

"你把这张纸条交给德·莫班夫人。"我说，"明天凌晨两点钟，你必须把新城堡的正门打开，告诉别的人你想透透空气，或者别的什么——然后就逃走。"

约翰显然很害怕，但是他看上去听懂了。我把我的计划告诉了萨普特和弗里茨。

sick adj. ill, not well. 病了，得病的。

81

'When Johann opens the front door,' I said, 'Sapt and his men will run into the castle and hold the men who are sleeping there. At the same time Antoinette will scream loudly again and again. She'll cry "Help! Help me, Michael!" And she'll shout Rupert of Hentzau's name. Duke Michael will hear and he'll run out of his room – straight into the hands of Sapt! Sapt will get the key from the Duke and let down the drawbridge. Rupert and De Gautet will hear the noise and hurry to cross the drawbridge. I'll hide by the bridge in the moat, and when they try to cross, I'll kill them. Then we'll hurry to the room where the King is, and kill Detchard and Bersonin before they have time to kill the King.'

The others listened in silence. It was a very dangerous plan, and I did not really think it would work – but we had to try!

That evening I went to visit Flavia. She seemed very thoughtful, and as I was leaving, she placed a ring on my finger. I was wearing the King's ring, but I took off my Rassendyll family ring and gave it to her. 'Wear this for me always,' I said.

She kissed the ring, and replied seriously, 'I'll wear it until the day I die.'

And then I had to leave her. I had already told the Marshal that if anything happened to the King, he must take Flavia to Strelsau, tell the people that Duke Michael had killed the King – and that Flavia was their Queen. I knew this could be my last day alive.

"等约翰打开正门，"我说，"萨普特和他的人就冲进去抓住睡在那儿的人。同时，安冬纳特就会不停地大声尖叫：'救命！救救我，迈克尔！'然后她会叫鲁帕特的名字。迈克尔公爵听见了就会冲出房间——正好落进萨普特的手里。萨普特就从公爵那儿拿到钥匙，放下吊桥。鲁帕特和德·高蒂特听见动静会冲过吊桥，我就藏在桥边的护城河里，他们过桥时我就除掉他们。然后我们就冲到国王在的那个房间里，在戴查德和伯索宁杀死国王之前先杀死他们。"

其他人静静地听着。这是一个非常危险的计划。我自己也并不真的相信它能成功。可我们必须试试！

那天晚上我去看望弗蕾维亚。她看上去心事重重。当我离开时她将一个戒指给我戴在手上。我戴着国王的戒指，但我摘下我的拉森狄尔家族的戒指给了她："永远替我戴着它吧。"我说。

她亲吻了戒指，严肃地回答："我会到死都戴着它的。"

我不得不离开她了。我已经告诉元帅，如果国王出了什么事，他必须把弗蕾维亚带回斯特莱索，告诉人民是迈克尔公爵杀死了国王——然后弗蕾维亚将成为他们的女王。我知道这也许是我生命中的最后一天了。

scream v. give a loud, sharp cry or cries. 尖叫。 **straight** adv. directly, without turning aside, without delay. 直接地，笔直地。 **work** v. (of a plan, machine etc.) to be active in a proper way. (计划等)奏效。 **thoughtful** adj. full of thought, showing thought. 深思的。 **wear** v. to have on the body. 穿，戴，佩。

12
The prisoner and the King

We needed bad weather, but it was a fine, clear night. At midnight Sapt, Fritz, and their men left and rode quietly through the woods towards the castle. If everything went well, they would get there at a quarter to two and wait for Johann to open the front door. If Johann did not open the door, Fritz would come round to the other side of the castle to find me. If I was not there, then I was dead — and the King, too! Sapt and his men would go back to Tarlenheim House and return with the Marshal and more men to get into the castle.

So, half an hour later, I, too, left Tarlenheim. I took a shorter way than Sapt and when I reached the moat, I hid my horse in the trees, tied my rope round a strong tree and let myself down into the water. Slowly, I began to swim along under the castle walls. Just after a quarter to one, I came to the pipe and waited quietly in its shadow. Light was coming from Duke Michael's window opposite me across the moat, and I could see into the room. The next window along, which Johann had said was Antoinette's room, was dark.

Then the Duke's window opened, and Antoinette de Mauban looked out. Behind her there was a man. Rupert of Hentzau! What was he doing in the Duke's room? I wondered.

Rupert tried to put his arm round Antoinette, but she moved

84

12 囚徒与国王

　　我们需要坏天气，但那天却是个晴朗的夜晚。午夜时分，萨普特、弗里茨和他们的人骑马出发了。他们悄悄穿过树林奔向城堡。如果一切顺利的话，他们一点三刻会到达那儿，等待约翰打开大门。如果约翰没开门，弗里茨就绕到城堡的另一面来找我。要是我不在那儿，那我就是死了——国王也一样。萨普特和他的人就回塔伦汉姆庄园，然后随同元帅一起带着更多的人去攻打城堡。

　　于是，半小时以后我也离开了塔伦汉姆庄园。比起萨普特来我抄了一条近路。到了护城河，我在树林里藏好马，把绳子系在一棵粗壮的树上，然后下到水里。慢慢地，我开始沿着城墙游着，差一刻一点的时候，我到了排水管边，在阴影里静静等待。河对岸正对着我的是迈克尔公爵的房间，灯光从窗户里照射出来。我可以看见屋子里面旁边的那扇窗子，照约翰所说，就是安冬纳特的房间了。那间屋子是黑的。

　　这时公爵的窗子打开了，安·德·莫班向外看着，她的身边有个男人，亨佐的鲁帕特！他在公爵的房间里做什么？我真想知道。

　　鲁帕特试图用胳膊去搂安冬纳特，可她

85

quickly away. At that moment, I heard the door of the room open and then the angry voice of Duke Michael.

'What are you doing here?' he cried.

'Waiting for you, sir,' Rupert replied quickly. 'I couldn't leave the lady alone.'

'Well, now you can go to bed. Are Detchard and Bersonin watching the prisoner?'

'Yes, sir.'

A few minutes later, Rupert crossed the drawbridge and it was pulled up. The light in Duke Michael's room went out, but a light came on, and stayed on, in Antoinette's room. In the silent darkness, I waited.

For about ten minutes everything was quiet, but suddenly I heard a noise on my side of the moat. A dark shape appeared in the gateway to the bridge, then turned and began to climb down some hidden steps in the wall. It was Rupert of Hentzau again — with a sword! Silently, he went down into the water and swam across the moat. Then he climbed out, and I heard him unlock the door. It was clear that Rupert of Hentzau had his own secret plans for that night.

It was not yet time for Johann to open the front door for my friends, and I still had to wait. I climbed up to the gateway of the bridge and hid in a dark corner. Now no one could enter or leave the old castle without fighting me. I wondered what Rupert was doing now, and a few seconds later I found out.

There was a sudden crash, and then a woman's screams rang

86

很快挪开了。就在此时,我听见房门打开了,然后听见迈克尔公爵气冲冲的声音:

"你在这儿干嘛?"他叫道。

"等着你呢,先生。"鲁帕特很快回答。"我不能让这位女士一个人呆着。"

"那好吧,现在你可以去睡觉了。戴查德和伯索宁在看着囚犯吗?"

"是的,先生。"

几分钟以后,鲁帕特走过吊桥,然后吊桥拉了起来。迈克尔房间的灯灭了,但是安冬纳特屋子的灯亮了,而且一直亮着。在寂静的黑暗里,我等待着。

大约过了十分钟什么声音也没有,可是突然我听到了在护城河我在的这一边有一点儿响动,一个黑影出现在通向吊桥的城门边,然后转过身开始顺着藏在墙里的台阶往下爬,是亨佐的鲁帕特,而且他手里还拿着剑! 他悄悄地下到水里,游过护城河,然后爬了上去。我听见他打开了门锁。很显然,鲁帕特当夜也有他自己的秘密计划。

现在还没有到约翰为我的朋友打开大门的时候,我还得等待。我从水里爬上对着吊桥的那座城门,在一个黑暗的角落里藏着。无论谁想进入老城堡或离开它,都得经过我这一关。我很想知道鲁帕特正在做什么。几秒钟后我就明白了。

突然响起了碰撞声,然后一个女人的尖

unlock *v. to unfasten the lock of.* 打开锁。**crash:** (*noise made by a*) *violent fall, blow or breaking.* 碰撞声,撞击声。

through the night.

'Help me, Michael! Rupert of Hentzau!'

Those were the words that I had written for Antoinette! But these were screams of real fear and soon I heard shouts and the sound of fighting from Antoinette's room. Then Rupert appeared at the window. His back was towards me, but he was fighting. 'That's for you, Johann,' I heard him cry. Then, 'Come on, Michael!'

So Johann was in there too, fighting at the Duke's side! How could he open the door for Sapt now?

More of the Duke's men had run to the room and the noise of the fighting grew louder. Suddenly, Rupert gave a wild laugh, and with his sword in his hand, jumped from the window into the moat below.

At that moment the door of the old castle opened and De Gautet appeared beside me. I jumped at him with my sword, and a second later he fell dead in the doorway without a word or a sound.

Wildly, I searched his body for the keys. I found them, and in a minute I was in the first room, where Bersonin and Detchard were. But there was only Bersonin in the room. Before he had time to realize that I was there, I had killed him. Detchard had run into the King's room and locked the door behind him. I ran at it to break it down. But would I be in time? Was the King already dead?

The King was standing helplessly by the wall. But the doctor

叫在夜色中震响:"救救我,迈克尔! 鲁帕特!"

这正是我要安冬纳特说的话。但那尖叫却带着真正的恐惧,而且立刻听见从女人房间传出叫喊和打斗声。然后鲁帕特出现在窗口,他的背冲着我,可他正和人格斗。"这一剑是给你的,约翰。"我听见他说。然后又说,"来吧,迈克尔!"

原来约翰也在那儿,站在公爵那边为公爵而战! 现在他怎么可能去为萨普特开门?

更多公爵的人冲进房间,厮杀声更响了。突然,鲁帕特狂笑一声,手里握着剑,从窗子里跳出来,跳进了下面的护城河。

正在这时,老城堡的门开了,德·高蒂特出现在我身旁,我手握利剑向他跳过去,片刻之后他倒在门前死了,没能说出一个字或发出一点声响。

我疯了一样在他身上搜寻钥匙,我找到了。一瞬间我已经冲进了第一间屋子,伯索宁和戴查德呆着的那间屋子,但房间里只有伯索宁。还没等他明白过来我已经杀死了他。戴查德已经冲进了国王的房间,并从里面锁上了门。我冲上去砸开门。我还来得及吗? 国王是不是已经死了?

国王正无助地站在墙边,那位医生也在

ring v. give out a clear, musical sound as when metal vibrates. 发出金属震动般的鸣响。in time: not late, early enough. 及时。

was also in the room and the brave little man had thrown himself at Detchard. He gave his life for the King, because, as I entered, Detchard pulled himself free and drove his sword into the doctor's side. Then, with an angry shout, Detchard turned to me.

We fought long and hard. Detchard was an excellent swordsman, and I was growing tired. He drove me back against the wall, gave me a deep cut in the arm, and began to smile. In a second he would kill me.

Suddenly, the King realized who I was.

'Cousin Rudolf!' he cried. Then he picked up a chair and threw it at Detchard's legs. The Englishman, jumping to one side, turned his sword against the King, and with a cry the King fell to the ground. Detchard moved towards me again, stepped in the doctor's blood on the floor — and fell to the ground himself. I had him! A second later his body lay across the dead doctor.

But was the King dead? I had no time to find out, because just then I heard the noise of the drawbridge coming down. And that wild-cat Rupert of Hentzau was still alive. The King must wait for help while I fought his enemies. I ran out of the room and up the steps towards the drawbridge. And then I heard the sound of laughter — Rupert of Hentzau was laughing!

He was standing alone in the middle of the bridge. In the gateway on the far side stood a group of the Duke's men. They seemed too frightened to move.

里面,这个勇敢的小个子扑向戴查德,他为国王献出了自己的生命。等我冲进去时,戴查德已经挣脱出来,并将剑刺进医生的肋部,然后他怒喊一声转向我。

我们打了很久,非常激烈。戴查德是位优秀的剑客,而我却越来越疲惫,他逼得我退到了墙边,在我的胳膊上深深地刺了一剑,然后开始微笑。很快他就能杀死我了。

突然,国王认出了我是谁。

"鲁道夫表弟!"他叫道。随即抄起一张椅子扔向戴查德的腿。那个英国人跳到了一边,将手里的剑刺向国王。国王叫了一声倒在地上。戴查德又转身向我。可这时他踩上了地板上医生的鲜血,自己倒在了地上。我赢了! 片刻之间他的尸体就倒在死去的医生身上了。

国王死了吗? 我没时间去理会,因为就在此时我听到了吊桥放下的声音,而且那个如豹子般凶猛的鲁帕特还活着,国王只好等人来帮他的忙,我得去打败他的敌人。我冲出房间,跑上通往吊桥的台阶。然后我听见了笑声——鲁帕特在笑!

他一个人站在吊桥中间,远处桥头城门那儿站着一群公爵的人,他们看上去太害怕了,动弹不得。

throw oneself at sb.: *rush violently at sb.* 冲向,扑向。**side** *n. the right or left part of the body, esp. from the shoulder to the top of the leg.* 身体的两侧,肋部,肋旁。**swordsman**: *man skilled in the use of a sword.* 剑客,击剑家。**have** *v. beat, win an advantage over.* 打败,战胜。**wild-cat**: *any animal of the group that includes tigers, lions, panthers, and leopards.* 猫科动物,包括老虎,狮子,美洲豹和豹子。**frightened** *adj. afraid, alarmed.* 害怕的,惊恐的。

'Come out, Michael, you dog!' Rupert shouted.

But a woman's wild cry answered him. 'He's dead! He's dead!'

The men in the gateway moved to one side and a woman came forward. Her face was as white as her long dress, and her dark hair lay over her shoulders. In her hand she held a gun. The shot rang out, but she missed. Rupert laughed. Again Antoinette de Mauban faced him, her gun ready. But, before she could shoot, Rupert jumped over the side of the bridge, and down into the moat below.

At that moment I heard the sound of running feet inside the new castle – and the welcome voice of my old friend, Captain Sapt! Then I knew that the King was safe and needed me no more. I ran out on to the bridge and jumped down into the moat. I had business to finish with Rupert of Hentzau.

*   *   *

I swam hard and caught up with him round the corner of the old castle. He had found my rope, climbed out of the moat, and was already running towards the trees where I had left my horse.

I ran after him as fast as I could. He turned and saw me, and called out, laughing, 'Why, it's the play-actor!' But then, with a cry of surprise, he found my horse, and in a minute he was on its back.

'Get down!' I shouted. 'Stand and fight, like a man!'

He turned, waiting for me, and I ran at him with my sword.

92

"出来,迈克尔,你这条狗!"鲁帕特叫道。

可是一个女人的狂叫回答了他:"他死了! 他死了!"

城门旁的人挪向一旁,一个女人朝前走来,她的脸像她的长裙子一样白,她的黑头发披散在肩头,她手里端着一支枪,枪响了,但她没打中。鲁帕特笑了,安冬纳特又一次面向他,子弹上了镗,但在她开枪之前,鲁帕特越过桥边,跳进了下面的护城河。

就在此时我听见了新城堡中有人奔跑的声响——还有我的老朋友萨普特上尉高兴的声音。我知道国王还活着,而且再也不需要我了。我冲过吊桥,也跳进了护城河。我跟鲁帕特还有账没算完。

我拼命游着,在老城堡边上追上了他。他发现了我的绳子,爬出了护城河,正要跑向那片树林。树林里还有我的马。

我尽全力追赶。他回身看见了我,笑着喊道:"嘿,是那位演员!"可就在此时,他惊喜地叫了一声,他看见了我的马,刹那间他已骑在马背上了。

"下来!"我叫道:"站着跟我打,像条汉子!"

他转过身来,等着我。我握着剑冲过

---

catch up with: *to come up from behind, overtake*. 追上,赶上。

93

For a few minutes we fought wildly. Blood ran from his face where I had cut it, but I had fought too many fights that night. He would surely kill me now.

I was saved by Fritz, who came galloping round the castle to find me. When Rupert saw him coming, he knew he had no chance.

' Goodbye, Rudolf Rassendyll! ' he called. ' We ' ll meet again! '

And he rode away into the forest, laughing and singing... and still alive.

I fell to the ground. Blood was running again from the cut in my arm, and I could not stand. Fritz jumped down from his horse and lifted me in his arms.

' Dear friend! ' he said. ' Thank God I've found you! When Johann did not come, we had to break down the castle door. We were afraid we would be too late. '

' And the King...? ' I said.

' Thanks to a very brave Englishman, ' Fritz said gently, ' the King is alive. '

去,一转眼我们就疯了似地打在一起了。他的脸上被我刺伤的地方血流了出来。但我那天晚上已经断杀了好多次,现在他肯定会杀了我。

是弗里茨救了我。他骑马绕着城堡找我。当鲁帕特见他过来时,就明白没有机会了。

"再见,鲁道夫·拉森狄尔!"他说:"我们会再见面的!"

然后他骑马跑进了树林,一边笑一边唱……他还活着。

我倒在地上,血又从我胳膊上的伤口流出来,我站不住了。弗里茨跳下马抱起我。

"亲爱的朋友!"他说:"感谢上帝我找到了你!约翰没来开门,我们只好砸开城堡的门。我们真担心太迟了。"

"国王呢?"我问。

"多亏了一位勇敢的英国人,"弗里茨轻柔地说,"国王还活着。"

thanks to: *as the result of, owing to.* 由于,幸亏。

95

13
Goodbye to Ruritania

Old Sapt worked hard to keep our secret hidden. He sent messages, told lies, and gave orders. All his plans were successful, except one. Nothing can stop a woman in love.

When Princess Flavia heard that the King was hurt, she refused to stay at Tarlenheim House and rode at once to the Castle of Zenda. Sapt had hidden me in a room in the old castle, and he and Fritz brought her to me there. How happy she was to see me! She threw her arms round my neck and kissed me.

'No!' cried Sapt. 'It's not the King. Don't kiss him. He is the man you love – but he is not the King!'

Flavia's face went white. 'What do you mean?' she cried. She turned to me again. 'Rudolf! Why do you let them say these things?'

I looked deeply into her eyes.

'It's true,' I said quietly. 'I am not the King.'

For a minute she continued to hold on to me. She looked at Sapt, at Fritz, and finally at me again. Then, slowly, she fell forward and I laid her gently on the ground.

'I wish that Rupert had killed me,' I said.

*   *   *

I saw the King once more. He thanked me, and I gave him back the royal Elphberg ring. If he noticed Flavia's ring on my finger, he said nothing. We both knew that we would never

96

13 告别卢里塔尼亚

老萨普特花了很大力气使我们的秘密不泄露出去。他发布消息,撒谎,下命令。他的所有计划都成功了,只有一件事除外。什么也阻挡不了一个恋爱中的女人。

当弗蕾维亚公主听说国王受了伤,她拒绝呆在塔伦汉姆庄园,而是立刻骑马赶来曾达城堡。萨普特把我藏在城堡的一间房子里,他和弗里茨把她带到我这儿。当她见到我时她是多么幸福啊! 她搂住我的脖子亲吻我。

"不!"萨普特叫道:"他不是国王,别亲他。他是你爱的那个男人,但他不是国王!"

弗蕾维亚的脸白了:"你是什么意思?"她叫道,她又转脸对着我:"鲁道夫! 为什么你允许他们说这些?"

我深深地看着她的眼睛:

"这是真的。"我平静地说:"我不是国王。"

有一会儿她仍然搂着我。她看看萨普特,弗里茨,最后又看着我,然后,慢慢地,她倒下了。我把她轻轻地放在地上。

"我真希望鲁帕特杀死了我。"我说。

我又一次见到了国王。他谢了我。我把艾尔弗伯格的王室戒指还给他。即使他看见弗蕾维亚的戒指戴在我的手上,他也没说什么。我们都知道我们再也不会相见了。

successful *adj*. *having gained a purpose or reached an aim*. 成功的,达到目的的。**except** *prep*. *not including*, *leaving out*, *but one*. 不包括,只除了……之外。

meet again.

Before I left Ruritania, Princess Flavia asked to see me again, and Fritz took me to her. They had told her everything.

We had so much to say – and so little to say. A princess is not free to choose who to love.

'Flavia,' I said, 'I love you. I'll love you until the day I die.'

As I walked away, I heard her say my name again and again. 'Rudolf... Rudolf...' I can hear it now.

*   *   *

I live quietly now, but every year Fritz and I meet in a little town outside Ruritania. There, he gives me news of the Queen of Ruritania, the wife of King Rudolf the Fifth. And every year he brings me a red rose and a note with the words written: *Rudolf – Flavia – always*. And I send her a red rose with the same message.

Shall I ever see her again? Who knows?

在我离开卢里塔尼亚之前,弗蕾维亚公主请求再见我一面。弗里茨带我去见她,他们把一切都告诉了她。

我们有这么多话可说——然而又没什么可说的。一位公主是没有权利自由选择爱什么人的。

"弗蕾维亚,"我说,"我爱你。我会一直爱你直到我死的那一天。"

我离开的时候,我听见她一遍又一遍叫我的名字:"鲁道夫⋯⋯鲁道夫⋯⋯"我现在还能听见。

如今我过着平静的生活。不过每年在靠近卢里塔尼亚的一座小城里,我和弗里茨会见上一面。在那儿,他告诉我关于卢里塔尼亚王后的消息,她是鲁道夫五世的妻子。每年她都给我一枝红玫瑰,还有一张纸条,上面写着"鲁道夫——弗蕾维亚——永远!"而我也送给她一枝红玫瑰,还有同样的字条。

我会再见到她吗?谁知道呢?

choose *v. to pick out from a great number.* 挑选,选择。

Exercises

A Checking your understanding

Chapters 1 – 2 *Who said these words in the story?*

1 'I'm so pleased that Robert's hair is black!'

2 'I like being an Elphberg.'

3 'Tonight we'll enjoy ourselves.'

Chapters 3 – 4 *Who in the story...*

1 ...carried the King to a room underground?

2 ...was not happy to see Rudolf in Strelsau?

3 ...warned Rudolf to be careful of Michael?

4 ...rode through the night to Zenda?

Chapters 5 – 6 *Write answers to these questions.*

1 Why did Rudolf have to go back to Strelsau?

2 What did Rudolf think was his greatest danger?

3 How did Rudolf escape from the house in New Avenue?

Chapters 7 – 9 *Are these sentences true (T) or false (F)?*

1 Sapt did not want Rudolf to ask Flavia to marry him.

2 Flavia loved Rudolf.

3 Duke Michael's men killed Bernenstein.

4 Rupert of Hentzau tried to kill Rudolf.

Chapters 10 – 11 *How much can you remember? Check your* *answers*.

1 How did Rudolf get to the pipe which came out of the prison?

2 How many men were killed that night?

3 Who took a note from Rudolf to Antoinette de Mauban?

Chapters 12 – 13 *Find answers to these questions in the text*.

1 Why didn't Johann open the door for Sapt and his men?

2 Why did Antoinette de Mauban try to kill Rupert of Hentzau?

3 Why did Rudolf chase after Rupert of Hentzau?

4 What did Princess Flavia do when she heard that Rudolf was hurt?

B Working with language

1 *Complete these sentences with information from the story*.

1 The King and Rudolf were surprised when they met because...

2 Antoinette didn't want Duke Michael to marry the princess, so...

3 Duke Michael offered Rudolf a hundred thousand pounds, but...

2 *Use these words to join each pair of sentences together*.

and then   because   when   but

1 Rudolf was a Rassendyll. He had the Elphberg hair and nose.

2 The King had disappeared. Sapt and Rudolf arrived back at the house in the forest.

3 Rudolf put his hands behind his back. He didn't want to shake hands with Rupert.

4 'They will kill the King. They will push the body down the pipe.'

C Activities

1 Which person do you like most in the story? Why? Write a few lines to describe this person.

2 Write Rupert of Hentzau's diary for the day when he tried to kill Rudolf Rassendyll at Tarlenheim House.

3 You are a newspaper reporter in Strelsau, and one year you secretly follow Fritz to his meeting with Rudolf outside Ruritania. Then you look at photographs of the King at his coronation, and at his wedding, and you begin to wonder. Write a report for your newspaper. Perhaps it begins like this:

Is there a secret in the royal family? Every year Fritz von Tarlenheim has a meeting with a man who has dark red hair and a long straight nose. Who is this man? He is not the King, but...

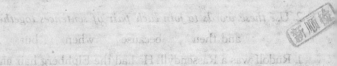